BUILDING CONSTRUCTION RELATED TO THE FIRE SERVICE

Instructional Developers
Justin House
Melissa Noakes

Senior Editor
Libby Hieber

Based on the Manual
validated by the International Fire
Service Training Association

Published by
Fire Protection Publications
Oklahoma State University

RECYCLABLE

Table of Contents

How to Use this Workbook

The **Building Construction Related to the Fire Service Course Workbook** accompanies the third edition of the IFSTA **Building Construction Related to the Fire Service** manual.

This workbook is designed to work in a number of ways. The workbook can be used as a study guide for self-study. Although the answers are not included in this book, the page numbers are included that reference the manual pages on which the answers can be found. The workbook may also be used as a homework assignment given by your instructor. In either case, the best approach to using this workbook is to read the questions through in their entirety, answer those questions that you can answer on your own, and look up those questions that you cannot answer in the manual.

The answers to the questions in this workbook can be found on the **Building Construction Related to the Fire Service** third edition Curriculum CD. If portions of this workbook are assigned as homework, your instructor will have access to these answers.

If you have any questions about this product or any of the **Building Construction Related to the Fire Service** third edition family of products, call Fire Protection Publications at 800.654.4055 or visit our website at www. IFSTA.org.

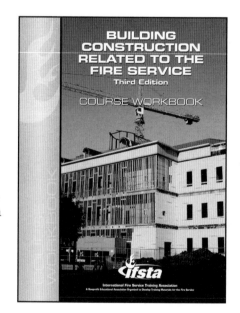

Chapter 1

Building Construction and the Fire Service

Terms

Write the definition of the terms below on the blanks provided.

1. Gentrification (12) _____

   _____

2. Fuel Loading (13) _____

   _____

3. Exposure (17) _____

   _____

4. Conflagration (17) _____

   _____

5. Setback (18) _____

   _____

6. Wildland/Urban Interface (18) _____

   _____

7. Convection (18) _____

   _____

8. Thermal Radiation (19) _____

   _____

9. Spec Building (24) _____

   _____

10. Aesthetics (26) _____

_____

11. Building Code (28)_____

_____

12. Area of Refuge (30) _____

_____

13. Green Design (32) _____

_____

14. Board of Appeals (36) _____

_____

15. Preincident Planning (40) _____

_____

True/False

Write True or False on the blanks provided; if False, write the correct statement on the lines provided.

_____ 1. In colonial America, buildings were originally built using thatched roofs and post and beam construction. (10)

_____

_____

_____ 2. As the 18th century ended, technology allowed the introduction of cast iron for columns and, later, steel for columns and beams. (10)

_____

_____

_____ 3. The age of a building is not itself a hazard, but age is often an indication of potential hazards. (12)

_____

_____

_____ 4. Older neighborhoods sometimes undergo aesthetics in which older properties are extensively rehabilitated to satisfy the desires of a modern real estate market. (12)

_____

_____

_____ 5. The configuration of a building refers to its general shape or layout. (15)

_____

_____

_____ 6. The National Fire Protection Association® (NFPA®) defines a building as an exposure when the heat from an external fire might cause ignition of or damage to the exposed building. (17)

_____

_____

_____ 7. Convection is the transfer of heat energy through space by electromagnetic waves. (19)

_____

_____

_____ 8. The collapse of a building under fire conditions is a result of the loss of a building's structural integrity. (21)

_____

_____

_____ 9. Fire-resistive material does not possess the ability to maintain structural integrity. (21)

_____

_____

_____ 10. Building codes impose restrictions on designers that may conflict with their creative desires. (28)

_____

_____

_____ 11. In a fast-track project, the design and construction phases overlap. (37)

_____

_____

_____ 12. The role of the fire inspector is to actually perform operational testing of the fire protection system during construction of a building. (39)

_____

_____

Matching

Write the correct answers on the blanks provided.

_____ 1. Which construction type is constructed with heavy timber? (14)

_____ 2. Which construction type is constructed with fire-resistive material? (14)

_____ 3. Which construction type is constructed with a wood frame? (14)

_____ 4. Which construction type is constructed with protected noncombustible material or noncombustible material? (14)

_____ 5. Which construction type is constructed with the exterior protected? (14)

A. Type I
B. Type II
C. Type III
D. Type IV
E. Type V

Short Answer

Write the correct answers on the blanks provided.

1. What are the building variables that can affect the course of a fire? (11) _____

   _____

   _____

2. What are five methods used to protect buildings from exposing fires? (20) _____

   _____

   _____

   _____

   _____

   _____

3. List three potential sources of building failure under fire conditions. (21) _____

   _____

   _____

4. List the factors a designer must consider when designing and constructing a building. (25)

   _____

   _____

   _____

   _____

   _____

   _____

   _____

   _____

   _____

   _____

   _____

5. What are five elements in which specific fire safety provisions include requirements for building fire safety? (29) _____

_____

_____

_____

_____

6. What are the areas that occupational safety must be considered? (29) _____

_____

_____

_____

_____

7. List the impairments that qualify as disabilities under the Americans With Disabilities Act (ADA). (30) _____

_____

_____

_____

_____

_____

8. What are five specific building elements that must be designed to accommodate individuals with restricted abilities? (30) _____

_____

_____

_____

_____

9. In addition to architecture, list five technical specialists that are involved in the erection of buildings. (34-35)_____

_____

_____

_____

_____

10. What are the examples of structural problems to buildings that are weakened by work that is performed without regard to proper methods? (37) _____

_____

_____

_____

_____

_____

_____

Multiple Choice

Write the correct answers on the blanks provided.

_____ 1. The invention of the ___ permitted the shift from log construction to planks and boards. (10)
   A. axe
   B. drill
   C. chainsaw
   D. circular saw

_____ 2. Which of the following refers to a building's general shape or layout? (15)
   A. Occupancy
   B. Aesthetics
   C. Configuration
   D. Conflagration

_____ 3. Which of the following is used to refer to a structure or an object such as a propane tank or a pile of lumber to which a fire could spread? (17)
   A. Exposure
   B. Occupancy
   C. Spec building
   D. Area of refuge

_____ 4. Which of the following is the transfer of heat by the movement of liquids or gases, usually in an upward direction? (18)
   A. Radiation
   B. Convection
   C. Conduction
   D. Conflagration

_____ 5. Which of the following refers to a failure to provide a level of fire safety appropriate to the ultimate use of the building? (22)
   A. Gentrification
   B. Design deficiencies
   C. Structural integrity
   D. Fire-resistance rating

_____ 6. The overall design of a building, as well as the individual details, is determined by the: (25)
   A. cost.
   B. aesthetics.
   C. building use.
   D. building code.

_____ 7. Which of the following is a body of law that determines the minimum standards that buildings must meet in the interest of community safety and health? (28)
   A. Building code
   B. Building permit
   C. NFPA® 1001 standard
   D. Building safety guideline

_____ 8. What year was the Americans With Disabilities Act (ADA) signed into law in the US? (30)

A. 1975

B. 1980

C. 1990

D. 1995

_____ 9. Documentation of fire protection system test results should be maintained by the: (39)

A. fire marshal.

B. building owner.

C. building contractor.

D. fire prevention bureau.

_____ 10. Tactical firefighters can develop knowledge of building construction by means of a(n): (40)

A. aesthetic plan.

B. preincident plan.

C. inspector's report.

D. postincident plan.

1

Crossword Puzzle

Across

1 Distance from the street line to the front of a building.

4 Act of preparing to handle an incident at a particular location or a particular type of incident before an incident occurs.

5 Branch of philosophy dealing with the nature of beauty, art, and taste.

9 Group of people, with experience in fire prevention, building construction, and/or code enforcement legally constituted to arbitrate differences of opinion between fire inspectors and property owners, occupants or builders.

13 Amount of fuel present expressed quantitatively in terms of weight of fuel per unit area.

14 Process of restoring rundown or deteriorated properties by more affluent people.

15 Body of local law, adopted by states, countries, cities, or other governmental bodies to regulate the construction, renovation, and maintenance of buildings.

Down

2 Transmission or transfer of heat energy from one body to another body by electromagnetic waves.

3 Zone where structures and other human development meet undeveloped wildland fuels.

6 Structure or separate part of the fireground to which the fire could spread.

7 Transfer of heat by the movement of heated fluids or gases, usually in an upward direction.

8 Large, uncontrollable fire covering a considerable area and crossing natural fire barriers.

10 Area where persons who are unable to use stairs can temporarily wait for instructions or assistance during an emergency building evacuation.

11 Building built without a tenant or occupant.

12 Incorporation of such environmental principles as energy efficiency and environmentally friendly building materials into design and construction.

Chapter 2

Structural Fire Resistance and Building Classifications

Terms

Write the definition of the terms below on the blanks provided.

1. Fire Resistance Rating (46)_____

   _____

2. Underwriters Laboratories, Inc. (UL) (49) _____

   _____

3. Fire Stop (50) _____

   _____

4. Fire Resistance Directory (51) _____

   _____

5. Noncombustible (53) _____

   _____

6. Masonry (54) _____

   _____

7. Light-Frame Construction (62) _____

   _____

8. Fire Load (63)_____

   _____

2

Write True or False on the blanks provided; if False, write the correct statement on the lines provided.

_____ 1. Fire resistance determines the likelihood of structural collapse under fire conditions. (45)

_____

_____

_____ 2. The combustible nature of a building's structural system will impact the rate of fire growth. (45)

_____

_____

_____ 3. A standardized test method for floor construction was adopted by the American National Standards Institute in 1907. (47)

_____

_____

_____ 4. The International Building Code® (IBC®) time-temperature test is the most commonly used method of satisfying building code requirements for structural fire resistance. (53)

_____

_____

_____ 5. NFPA® 220, _Standard on Types of Building Construction_, details the requirements for each of the building classifications and subclassifications. (54)

_____

_____

_____ 6. The most commonly used test for determining combustibility is ASTM E 136, _Standard Test Method for Behavior of Materials in a Vertical Tube Furnace at 750°C._ (54)

_____

_____

_____ 7. Type I construction is commonly referred to as "ordinary construction." (58)

_____

_____

_____ 8. Type III construction is frequently constructed with exterior walls of wood siding. (58)

_____

_____

_____ 9. Type III B construction is required to have a one-hour fire-resistive rating for interior members. (59)

_____

_____

_____ 10. The basic method of construction in a Type V building consists of using a wood frame to provide the primary structural support. (61)

_____

_____

_____ 11. The fire load can be used as an estimate of the total potential heat release of thermal energy to which a building may be subjected if all combustibles become fully involved in fire. (63)

_____

_____

_____ 12. Building codes classify buildings according to their fire load as well as their size. (63)

_____

_____

2

Short Answer

Write the correct answers on the blanks provided.

1. What are the three means by which the fire resistance of structural assemblies can be determined? (47) _____

    _____

    _____

2. List five organizations that perform fire-resistance testing. (50) _____

    _____

    _____

    _____

    _____

    _____

    _____

    _____

    _____

3. Explain what each of the numbers identify in the three-digit number code of NFPA® 220. (54) _____

    _____

    _____

4. List five ways in which combustible materials are permitted to be used in Type I construction. (57) _____

    _____

    _____

    _____

    _____

5. What are the two distinctions between Type III and IV construction? (60) _____

    _____

    _____

    _____

    _____

6. What are the ten International Building Code® (IBC®) major occupancy classifications?

    (64) _____

    _____

    _____

    _____

    _____

    _____

    _____

    _____

    _____

    _____

    _____

Identification

Identify the different types of construction on the lines provided.

1. _____

2. _____

3. _____

4. _____

5. _____

Multiple Choice

Write the correct answers on the blanks provided.

_____ 1. Which NFPA® standard is the standard method of tests of fire endurance of building construction and materials? (47)
  A. 119
  B. 251
  C. 1907
  D. 2009

_____ 2. Underwriters Laboratories annually publishes a ___, which lists assemblies that have been tested and their fire-resistance rating. (51)
  A. *Fire Stop Manual*
  B. *Fire Resistance Directory*
  C. *Noncombustible Directory*
  D. protected combustible material video

_____ 3. Which of the following is based on the material used in construction and the hourly fire-resistance rating required for the structural component? (54)
  A. Fire test
  B. Fire load
  C. Analytical calculation
  D. Building classification

_____ 4. Which of the following is classified as fire-resistive construction? (55)
  A. Type I
  B. Type II
  C. Type III
  D. Type IV

_____ 5. What are the two most common methods of constructing Type I construction buildings? (57)
  A. Wood frame and masonry
  B. Reinforced concrete and wood frame
  C. Protected steel frame and heavy timber
  D. Reinforced concrete and protected steel frame

_____ 6. Which of the following construction classifications is commonly referred to as ordinary construction? (58)
   A. Type I
   B. Type II
   C. Type III
   D. Type IV

_____ 7. Which of the following types of Type III construction is required to have a one-hour fire-resistive rating for interior members? (59)
   A. Type III A
   B. Type III B
   C. Type III C
   D. Type III D

_____ 8. Which of the following classifications of construction is commonly known as heavy-timber or "mill" construction? (60)
   A. Type I
   B. Type II
   C. Type III
   D. Type IV

_____ 9. Which of the following classifications of construction is commonly known as wood-frame construction? (61)
   A. Type II
   B. Type III
   C. Type IV
   D. Type V

_____ 10. Type V structures are required to have a ___ -hour fire resistance rating for the structural members. (61)
   A. 1
   B. 2
   C. 3
   D. 4

_____ 11. Which of the following types of construction has eliminated heavy posts and beams and made use of smaller studs, joists, and rafters? (62)
   A. Mixed   C. Light-framed
   B. Ordinary   D. Noncombustible

_____ 12. Ordinary combustibles such as wood, paper, and similar materials have heats of combustion between ___ BTU per pound (J/kg). (63)
   A. 5,000 and 6,000 (11,630 to 13,955)
   B. 6,000 and 7,000 (13,955 to 16,282)
   C. 7,000 and 8,000 (16,282 to 18,608)
   D. 8,000 and 9,000 (18,608 to 20,933)

_____ 13. The International Building Code® (IBC®) contains ___ major occupancy classifications. (64)
   A. 5
   B. 10
   C. 15
   D. 20

_____ 14. NFPA® 5000, _Building Construction and Safety Code_, and NFPA® 101, _Life Safety Code®_, make use of ___ major occupancy classifications. (65)
   A. 3
   B. 6
   C. 9
   D. 12

Crossword Puzzle

Across

3 Solid materials used to prevent or limit the vertical and horizontal spread of fire.

4 Bricks, blocks, stones, and unreinforced and reinforced concrete products.

6 Amount of time a material will resist a typical fire as measured on a standard time-temperature curve.

7 Independent fire research and testing laboratory.

Down

1 Directory that lists building assemblies that have been tested and given fire resistance ratings.

2 Method for construction of wood-frame buildings.

5 Incapable of supporting combustion under normal circumstances.

6 Used as a measure of the potential heat release of a fire within a compartment.

Chapter 3

The Way Buildings Are Built: Structural Design Features

Terms

Write the definition of the terms below on the blanks provided.

1. Load (72) _____

_____

2. Gravity (72) _____

_____

3. Kinetic Energy (73) _____

_____

4. Seismic Forces (75) _____

_____

5. Inertia (77) _____

_____

6. Damping Mechanism (79) _____

_____

7. Dead Load (81) _____

_____

8. Live Load (82) _____

_____

9. Concentrated Load (82) _____

_____

10. Static Load(s) (84) _____

_____

11. Dynamic Load (84) _____

_____

12. Equilibrium (85) _____

_____

13. Cantilever (87) _____

_____

14. Tension (87) _____

_____

15. Failure Point (88) _____

_____

16. Axial Load (88) _____

_____

17. Eccentric Load (89) _____

_____

18. Torsional Load (89) _____

_____

19. Beam (90) _____

_____

20. Column (93) _____

_____

21. Truss (95) _____

_____

22. Bearing Wall (98)_____

_____

23. Surface System (101) _____

_____

24. Membrane Structure (101) _____

_____

25. Shell Structure (102) _____

_____

True/False

Write True or False on the blanks provided; if False, write the correct statement on the lines provided.

_____   1. Gravity creates a force on a building through the weight of the building's components and all of its contents. (72)

_____

_____

_____   2. Wind passing over a surface such as a roof may cause vibration of the surface depending on the velocity of the wind and the harmonic characteristics of the surface. (73)

_____

_____

_____   3. In designing buildings to withstand the force of wind, the primary effect considered is the force due to negative pressure. (73)

_____

_____

_____ 4. Firefighters should be alert for unbraced walls at demolition sites and at fire-damaged buildings where interior structural supports have collapsed or been destroyed. (74)

_____

_____

_____ 5. Earthquakes occur as a result of slippage between the tectonic plates that make up the earth's surface. (75)

_____

_____

_____ 6. The movement of the ground beneath a building can be three-dimensional, and the vertical motion is the most significant force. (77)

_____

_____

_____ 7. As the ground moves under a building, shear force tends to keep the upper portion of the building momentarily in its initial position. (77)

_____

_____

_____ 8. Buildings with geometric irregularities are inherently more susceptible to damage from earthquakes than buildings having a symmetrical design. (77)

_____

_____

_____ 9. A concentrated load is one that is applied at one point or over a small area. (82)

_____

_____

_____ 10. Rain and snow are considered dead loads on a building's roof. (83)

_____

_____

_____ 11. When the support provided by a structural system is equal to the applied loads, a condition known as equilibrium exists. (85)

_____

_____

_____ 12. A beam that is supported at one end is known as a tension beam. (87)

_____

_____

_____ 13. The failure point of a material is the stress at which it fails to perform satisfactorily. (88)

_____

_____

_____ 14. A restrained beam is supported at each end and is free to rotate at the ends. (90)

_____

_____

_____ 15. In an I-beam, the top and bottom portions of the beam are known as the top and bottom flanges. (92)

_____

_____

_____ 16. Arches are used to carry loads across a distance and have application as support for roofs and entrances in masonry buildings. (93)

_____

_____

_____ 17. Trusses can be thought of as flexible structural members that can be used to support roofs, brace tents, and restrain pneumatic structures. (94)

_____

_____

_____ 18. In a bearing wall structure, the walls are subjected to compressive loads. (98)

_____

_____

_____ 19. In the fire service, it is not uncommon to use the term frame construction to refer to a wood-frame building. (99)

_____

_____

_____ 20. When the joints between a column and a beam are reinforced so bending stresses can be transmitted through the joints, the structural system is known as truss frame. (100)

_____

_____

Short Answer

Write the correct answers on the blanks provided.

1. What are the factors that affect the magnitude of forces developed within a building during an earthquake? (76-77) _____

_____

2. List the buildings that are essential for community recovery after an earthquake. (78)

_____

_____

3. What are the two isolation methods used to isolate buildings from the horizontal movements of the earth's surface? (79) _____

_____

4. What are the two types of loads resulting from gravity? (81)_____

_____

_____

5. What are five components that are used to construct larger structural systems? (90)

_____

_____

_____

_____

_____

Identification

Write the correct answers on the blanks provided.

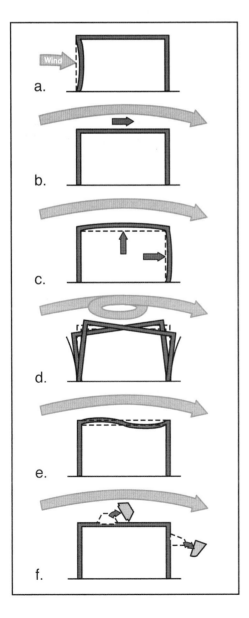

1. Identify the effects of wind. (74)

a. _____

b. _____

c. _____

d. _____

e. _____

f. _____

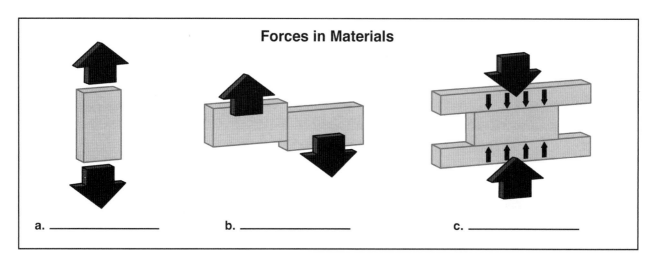

Forces in Materials

a. _____

b. _____

c. _____

2. Identify the interior forces according to the direction in which they occur. (88)

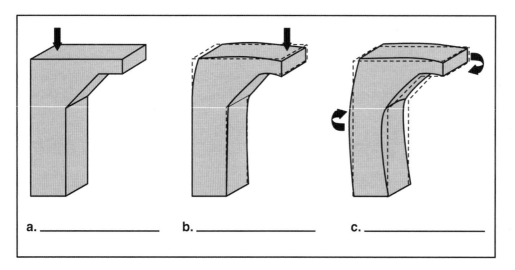

a. _____

b. _____

c. _____

3. Identify the different load types. (89)

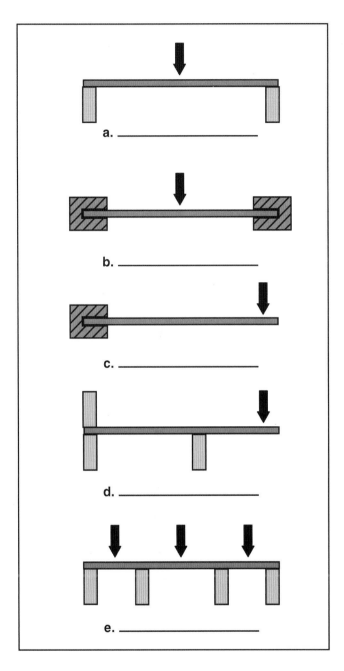

a. _____

b. _____

c. _____

d. _____

e. _____

4. Identify how the beams are supported. (91)

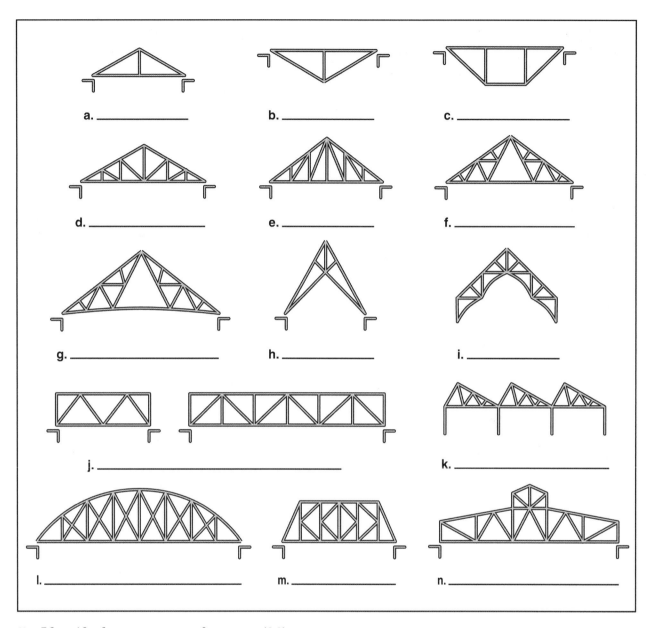

a. _____

b. _____

c. _____

d. _____

e. _____

f. _____

g. _____

h. _____

i. _____

j. _____

k. _____

l. _____

m. _____

n. _____

5. Identify the common roof trusses. (96)

Matching

Write the correct answers on the blanks provided.

_____1. Tends to pull the material apart (87)

_____2. Tends to slide one plane of a material past an adjacent plane (87)

_____3. Tends to squeeze the material (87)

A. Tension
B. Compression
C. Shear

Multiple Choice

Write the correct answers on the blanks provided.

_____ 1. Which of the following is defined as any effect (or force) that a structure must resist? (72)
A. Load
B. Gravity
C. Energy
D. Negative pressure

_____ 2. Which of the following describes the impact effect the wind has on a surface? (73)
A. Vibration
B. Rocking effects
C. Direct pressure
D. Negative pressure

_____ 3. Which of the following describes when wind encounters an object, and its fluid nature causes it to flow around the object? (73)
A. Rocking effects
B. Direct pressure
C. Clean-off effect
D. Aerodynamic drag

_____ 4. Which of the following is a suction effect produced on the downwind side of the building resulting in an outward pressure? (73)
A. Direct pressure
B. Clean-off effect
C. Negative pressure
D. Aerodynamic drag

_____ 5. Which of the following is a back-and-forth effect due to variations in the velocity of the wind? (73)
- A. Vibrations
- B. Rocking effects
- C. Clean-off effects
- D. Aerodynamic drag

_____ 6. Which of the following is the tendency of the wind to dislodge objects from a building? (73)
- A. Vibrations
- B. Rocking effects
- C. Clean-off effects
- D. Aerodynamic drag

_____ 7. Major earthquakes occur most frequently in parts of the world known as: (75)
- A. fault zones.
- B. gravitational zones.
- C. seismic probability zones.
- D. high geographic force zones.

_____ 8. Which of the following are forces in a structural member when it is twisted? (76)
- A. Seismic
- B. Resonant
- C. Torsional
- D. Gravitational

_____ 9. Which of the following are movements of relatively large amplitude resulting from a small force applied at the natural frequency of a structure? (76)
- A. Seismic
- B. Resonant
- C. Torsional
- D. Gravitational

_____ 10. Which of the following is pressure exerted by the soil against the foundation? (79)
- A. Shear force
- B. Damping pressure
- C. Active soil pressure
- D. Passive soil pressure

_____ 11. Which of the following is the force of the foundation against the soil? (79)
   A. Shear force
   B. Damping pressure
   C. Active soil pressure
   D. Passive soil pressure

_____ 12. Which of the following is the weight of any permanent part of a building? (81)
   A. Live load
   B. Dead load
   C. Static load
   D. Concentrated load

_____ 13. Which of the following is any load that is not fixed or permanent? (82)
   A. Live load
   B. Dead load
   C. Static load
   D. Concentrated load

_____ 14. Which of the following are loads that are steady or are applied gradually? (84)
   A. Live loads
   B. Static loads
   C. Dynamic loads
   D. Concentrated loads

_____ 15. Which of the following are loads that involve motion? (84)
   A. Dead loads
   B. Static loads
   C. Dynamic loads
   D. Concentrated loads

_____ 16. The forces that resist the applied loads are known as: (86)
   A. stresses.
   B. reactions.
   C. internal forces.
   D. dynamic loads.

3

17. Which of the following is a load applied to the center of the cross section of a structural member and perpendicular to that cross section? (88)
    A. Axial load
    B. Eccentric load
    C. Torsional load
    D. Compression load

18. Which of the following is a load that is perpendicular to the cross section of the structural member but does not pass through the center of the cross section? (89)
    A. Axial load
    B. Eccentric load
    C. Torsional load
    D. Compression load

19. Which of the following is offset from the center of the cross section of the structural member and at an angle to or in the same plane as the cross section? (89)
    A. Axial load
    B. Eccentric load
    C. Torsional load
    D. Compression load

20. Which of the following is a structural member that can carry loads perpendicular to its longitudinal dimension? (90)
    A. Arche
    B. Beam
    C. Truss
    D. Space frame

21. Which of the following are structural members designed to support an axial compressive load? (93)
    A. Beams   C. Trusses
    B. Arches   D. Columns

22. Which of the following is a curved structural member in which the interior stresses are primarily compressive? (93)
    A. Beam
    B. Arch
    C. Truss
    D. Column

23. Which of the following are framed structural units made up of a group of triangles in one plane? (95)
    A. Beams
    B. Arches
    C. Trusses
    D. Columns

24. Which of the following construction uses a series of vertical elements to support horizontal elements that are subject to transverse loads? (99)
    A. Truss frame
    B. Rigid frame
    C. Post and beam
    D. Steel stud wall frame

25. Which of the following are most frequently encountered in concrete structures? (101)
    A. Truss frames
    B. Rigid frames
    C. Slab and column frames
    D. Post and beam construction

3

Crossword Puzzle

BUILDING CONSTRUCTION RELATED TO THE FIRE SERVICE COURSE WORKBOOK

Across

4 Load perpendicular to the cross section of the structural member but does not pass through the center of the cross section.

5 Vertical supporting member.

7 Tendency of a body to remain in motion or at rest until it is acted upon by force.

9 Vertical or horizontal forces that tend to pull things apart.

11 Force placed upon a structure by the addition of people, objects, or weather.

12 Loads that are steady, motionless constant, or applied gradually.

13 Structural member used to form a roof or floor framework.

14 System of construction in which the building consists primarily of an enclosing surface and in which the stresses resulting from the applied loads occur within the surface bearing wall structures.

19 Load offset from the center of the cross section of the member and at an angle to or in the same plane as the cross section.

20 Point at which material ceases to perform satisfactorily.

22 Structure with an enclosing surface of a thin stretched flexible material.

23 Load applied to the center of the cross-section of a member and perpendicular to that cross section.

Down

1 Load on a structure due to its own weight and other fixed weights.

2 Forces developed by earthquakes.

3 Energy possessed by a moving object.

5 Load that is applied at one point or over a small area.

6 Force acting to draw an object toward the earth's center.

8 Rigid, three-dimensional structure having an outer "skin" thickness that is small compared to other dimensions.

10 Structural element designed to control vibration.

15 Condition in which the support provided by a structural system is equal to the applied loads.

16 Projecting beam or slab supported at one end.

17 Wall that supports itself and the weight of the roof and/or other internal structural framing components such as the floor beams above it.

18 Loads that involve motion.

21 Structural member subjected to loads, usually vertical, perpendicular to its length.

Chapter 4

Building Systems

Terms

Write the definition of the terms below on the blanks provided.

1. Means of Egress (109) _____

   _____

2. Convenience Stair (109) _____

   _____

3. Rise (109) _____

   _____

4. Run (109) _____

   _____

5. Scissor Stairs (112) _____

   _____

6. Protected Stair Enclosure (113) _____

   _____

7. Fire Escape (115) _____

   _____

8. Smokeproof Enclosures (116) _____

   _____

9. Americans with Disabilities Act (ADA) of 1990 - Public Law 101-336 (119)

   _____

   _____

10. Mushrooming (122) _____

_____

11. Blind Hoistway (123) _____

_____

12. Pipe Chase (126) _____

_____

13. Refuse Chute (128) _____

_____

14. Heating, Ventilating, and Air Conditioning (HVAC) System (129) _____

_____

15. Duct (134) _____

_____

16. Interstitial Space (134)_____

_____

17. Smoke Control System (135)_____

_____

18. Curtain Boards (141) _____

_____

19. Voltage (142) _____

_____

20. Dielectric (143) _____

_____

21. Generator (144) _____

_____

True/False

Write True or False on the blanks provided; if False, write the correct statement on the lines provided.

_____ 1. Stairs that are a part of the required means of egress must meet strict requirements of the applicable building code, and generally are either fully enclosed or protected open exterior stairs. (109)

_____

_____

_____ 2. Scissor stair design is common in modern construction. (110)

_____

_____

_____ 3. Folding stairs can serve as a vertical path for fire and smoke spread. (112)

_____

_____

_____ 4. Protecting the stairwell from the products of combustion is extremely important; building codes require a high level of protection for most stairs as a means of egress. (113)

_____

_____

_____ 5. Building codes have traditionally required a minimum of three smokeproof stair enclosures for stairs serving buildings five stories or higher. (116)

_____

_____

_____ 6. The Americans with Disabilities Act (ADA) has mandated that public buildings be made accessible to individuals with disabilities. (119)

_____

_____

_____ 7. Drum elevators are the most common type of elevator in buildings over six stories. (120)

_____

_____

_____ 8. An elevator hoistway is the vertical shaft in which the elevator car travels and includes the elevator pit. (122)

_____

_____

_____ 9. Passenger elevator car doors are powered by an electric motor mounted on top of the elevator car. (123)

_____

_____

_____ 10. The most common method of protecting the vertical opening is to use closely spaced sprinklers in conjunction with draft stops around the openings. (125)

_____

_____

_____ 11. A refuse chute is a type of utility chase used to contain piping needed for building services. (126)

_____

_____

_____ 12. A grease duct is installed as part of an exhaust system for commercial cooking appliances that produce grease-laden vapors. (129)

_____

_____

_____ 13. Curtain boards reduce the dissipation of the heated air currents from a fire and increase the speed of operation of the vents. (141)

_____

_____

_____ 14. Generators are typically engine-driven, using a gasoline, diesel, or natural gas internal combustion engine. (144)

_____

_____

_____ 15. Lead-acid batteries contain sulfuric acid and lead. (144)

_____

_____

Short Answer

Write the correct answers on the blanks provided.

1. What are the two most common forms of power to perform the hoisting and lowering operations of an elevator? (119) _____

_____

2. List five safety devices found on elevators. (121)_____

_____

_____

_____

_____

3. What are the components of an HVAC system? (133-134) _____

    _____

    _____

    _____

    _____

    _____

4. What are the two methods that can be used to protect an enclosed stairwell from smoke?
    (138) _____

    _____

5. What are the two general design methods used for pressurized stairwells? (139) _____

    _____

    _____

6. List the different names for lead-acid batteries. (145) _____

    _____

    _____

    _____

    _____

    _____

Identification

Write the correct answers on the blanks provided.

1. Identify the six types of stair designs. (111)

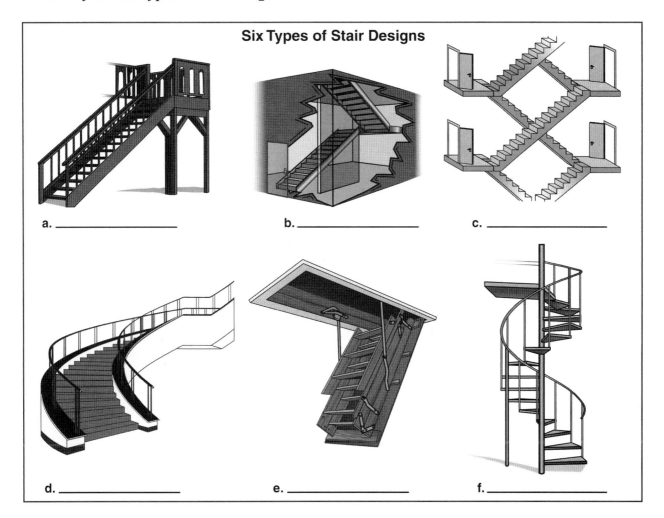

Six Types of Stair Designs

a. _____

b. _____

c. _____

d. _____

e. _____

f. _____

2. Identify the different types of hoistways. (122)

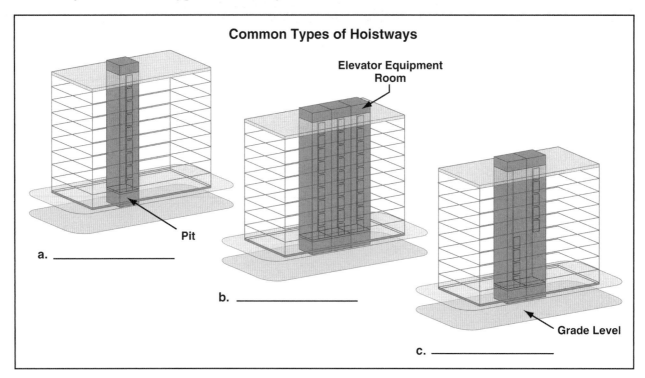

Common Types of Hoistways

Elevator Equipment Room

Pit

a. _____

b. _____

Grade Level

c. _____

3. Identify the components of an HVAC system. (132)

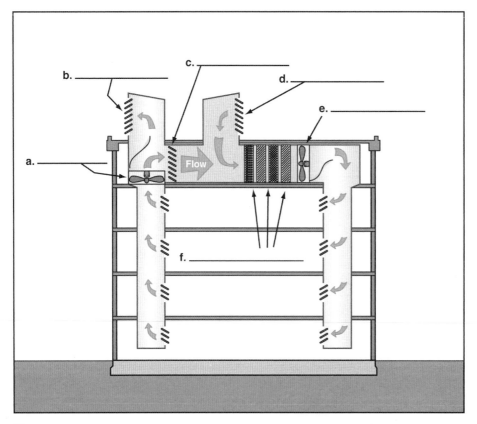

a. _____

b. _____

c. _____

d. _____

e. _____

Flow

f. _____

Multiple Choice

Write the correct answers on the blanks provided.

_____ 1. Which of the following types of stairs extend in a straight line for their entire length? (109)

    A. Return

    B. Folding

    C. Scissor

    D. Straight run

_____ 2. Which of the following types of stairs have an intermediate landing between floors and reverse directions at that point? (110)

    A. Spiral

    B. Return

    C. Folding

    D. Scissor

_____ 3. Which of the following types of stairs are two separate sets of stairs constructed in a common shaft? (110)

    A. Spiral

    B. Return

    C. Folding

    D. Scissor

_____ 4. Which of the following types of stairs are often found as grand stairs or convenience stairs serving only two levels? (112)

    A. Spiral

    B. Circular

    C. Folding

    D. Scissor

_____ 5. Which of the following types of stairs are typically found in dwellings where they are used to provide access to an attic space that does not have a permanent access stair? (112)

    A. Spiral

    B. Circular

    C. Folding

    D. Scissor

_____ 6. Which of the following types of stairs allow stairs to be placed in a very small space and consist of a series of steps spiraling around a single column? (113)

A. Spiral

B. Circular

C. Folding

D. Scissor

_____ 7. Which of the following hoistways are used for express elevators that serve the upper elevator zones in tall buildings? (123)

A. Blind

B. Single car

C. Lower floor

D. Multiple car

_____ 8. Which of the following contains procedures to follow in performing evacuations of an elevator? (124)

A. NFPA® 90A

B. NFPA® 1001

C. ASME Standard A17.4

D. Americans with Disabilities Act (ADA)

_____ 9. Which of the following are typically found in manufacturing or storage occupancies and are used to transport items and materials? (126)

A. Utility shafts

B. Vertical shafts

C. HVAC systems

D. Conveyor systems

_____ 10. Which of the following is the standard for installation of air-conditioning and ventilation systems? (131)

A. NFPA® 90A

B. NFPA® 250

C. NFPA® 472

D. NFPA® 1001

_____ 11. Which of the following are the air distribution components of HVAC systems? (134)

    A. Fans

    B. Air ducts

    C. Air filtrations

    D. Outside air intakes

_____ 12. Which of the following are used to convert high-voltage electricity to an appropriate voltage for use in the building? (142)

    A. Generators

    B. Transformers

    C. Lead-acid batteries

    D. Emergency power systems

4

Crossword Puzzle

BUILDING CONSTRUCTION RELATED TO THE FIRE SERVICE COURSE WORKBOOK

Across

5 Electrical force that causes a charge (electrons) to move through a conductor.

7 Nonconductor of direct electric current.

10 Safe, continuous path of travel from any point in a structure to a public way.

12 Means of escaping from a building in case of fire.

14 Stair with code required fire-rated enclosure construction.

16 Channel or enclosure, usually of sheet metal, used to move heating and cooling air through a building.

17 Stair that usually connects two floors in a multistory building.

19 Refers to generally inaccessible spaces between layers of building materials.

Down

1 Engineered system designed to control smoke.

2 Used for express elevators that serve only upper floors of tall buildings.

3 Stairways that are designed to limit the penetration of smoke, heat, and toxic gases from a fire on a floor of a building into the stairway and that serve as part of a means of egress.

4 Vertical shaft with a self-closing access door on every floor.

6 Auxiliary electrical power generating device.

8 Vertical distance between the treads of a stairway or the height of the entire stairway.

9 Tendency of heat, smoke, and other products of combustion to rise until they encounter a horizontal obstruction.

11 Concealed vertical channel in which pipes and other utility conduits are housed.

13 Vertical boards, fire-resistive half-walls, that extend down from the underside of the roof of some commercial buildings and are intended to limit the spread of fire, heat, smoke and fire gases.

15 Two sets of crisscrossing stairs in a common shaft.

18 Horizontal measurement of a stair tread or the distance of the entire stair length.

Chapter 5

Fire Behavior and Building Construction

Write the definition of the terms below on the blanks provided.

1. Interior Finish (153) _____

_____

2. Heat Release Rate (HRR) (156) _____

_____

3. Flame Spread Rating (156) _____

_____

4. Steiner Tunnel Test (156) _____

_____

5. Assembly (156) _____

_____

6. Toxicity (158) _____

_____

7. Volatility (158) _____

_____

8. Fire Retardant (159) _____

_____

9. Compartmentation System (162) _____

_____

10. Rated Assembly (162) _____

_____

11. Shelter in Place (162) _____

_____

12. Fire Wall (163) _____

_____

13. Fire Partition (166) _____

_____

14. Glazing (167) _____

_____

15. Curtain Wall (168) _____

_____

16. Fire Stop (169) _____

_____

17. Fire Door (170) _____

_____

True/False

Write True or False on the blanks provided; if False, write the correct statement on the lines provided.

_____ 1. The term interior finish is generally applied to the material used for the exposed face of the walls and ceilings of a building. (153)

_____

_____

_____ 2. The fire load is a measure of the total fuel available to a fire and the total heat that can be released in a fire. (156)

_____

_____

_____ 3. The Steiner Tunnel Test is not a commonly used method for evaluating the surface burning characteristics of materials. (156)

_____

_____

_____ 4. The flame spread rating is an absolute measure of the spread of fire travel. (157)

_____

_____

_____ 5. Fire-retardant coatings are valid treatments for the reduction of surface burning. (159)

_____

_____

_____ 6. ASTM E-104 test procedures to measure the surface burning characteristics of materials are useful because they provide reproducible results and are a widely recognized standard. (159)

_____

_____

_____ 7. Test procedures that incorporate the size and shape of real rooms are collectively known as corner tests. (160)

_____

_____

_____ 8. Fire-rated partitions can provide areas of refuge for occupants when immediate or rapid evacuation is not possible. (162)

_____

_____

_____ 9. Fire walls subdivide a building into small areas so that a fire in one portion of a building is limited to that area and does not destroy the entire building. (163)

_____

_____

_____ 10. Curtain walls are used to enclose such vertical openings as stairwells, elevator shafts, and pipe chases that extend from floor to floor in a building. (166)

_____

_____

_____ 11. Windows with fire-rated glazing cannot be used with stair enclosures. (167)

_____

_____

_____ 12. Curtain walls are often constructed using a combination of glass and steel. (168)

_____

_____

_____ 13. The letter designations of fire doors are still used today to describe the types of openings for which a door was intended. (171)

_____

_____

_____ 14. Rated fire doors are identified with a label indicating the door type, hourly rating, and the identifying label of the testing laboratory. (172)

_____

_____

_____ 15. A fire door has to be a solid door, because vision panels reduce its fire rating. (172)

_____

_____

Short Answer

Write the correct answers on the blanks provided.

1. List the ways combustibility of interior finish affects the behavior of fire. (153)_____

_____
_____
_____
_____
_____

2. What are the factors that influence the speed of flame spread over an interior finish? (154)

_____
_____
_____
_____

3. What are three types of fire-retardant coatings? (159) _____

_____
_____
_____
_____

4. List the devices that operate a fire door. (174) _____

_____

Multiple Choice

Write the correct answers on the blanks provided.

_____ 1. Class B materials have a flame spread rating of: (155)
   A. 0-25.
   B. 26-75.
   C. 76-200.
   D. 200-500.

_____ 2. Which of the following is the ability of a substance to do harm within the body? (158)
   A. Toxicity
   B. Volatility
   C. Assembly
   D. Flame

_____ 3. Which of the following is the ability of a substance to vaporize easily at a relatively low temperature? (158)
   A. Toxicity
   B. Volatility
   C. Assembly
   D. Flame spread rating

_____ 4. Which of the following consists of equipment such as automatic sprinkler systems or fire alarm systems that require a power source for operation? (161)
   A. Rated assembly
   B. Active fire protection
   C. Passive fire protection
   D. Compartmentation system

_____ 5. Which of the following relies on building construction and materials to contain fire or products of combustion? (161)
   A. Rated assembly
   B. Active fire protection
   C. Passive fire protection
   D. Compartmentation system

_____ 6. The subdivision of a building or the floor levels of a building by fire-rated walls or partitions is generally referred to as: (162)
   A. curtain walls.
   B. rated assembly.
   C. compartmentation.
   D. smokeproof tower.

_____ 7. The International Building Code® (IBC®) permits combustible structural members to be framed into a masonry or concrete fire wall from opposite sides provided there is a ___ inch (mm) separation between the ends of structural members. (165)
   A. 2 (50)
   B. 4 (100)
   C. 6 (150)
   D. 8 (200)

_____ 8. Which of the following are interior walls used to subdivide a floor or area of a building that do not qualify as fire walls? (166)

A. Fire partitions

B. Curtain boards

C. Smoke dampers

D. Smokeproof towers

_____ 9. The most common means for protecting openings through fire-rated walls is by the use of: (170)

A. fire doors.

B. curtain walls.

C. fire retardants.

D. forced air systems.

_____ 10. Which of the following types of fire doors are often used to protect an opening in a fire wall in an industrial occupancy? (175)

A. Special

B. Swinging

C. Rolling steel

D. Horizontal sliding

_____ 11. Which of the following types of fire doors are usually held open by a fusible link and slide into position along a track either by gravity or by force of a counterweight? (176)

A. Special

B. Swinging

C. Rolling steel

D. Horizontal sliding

_____ 12. Which of the following types of fire doors are common in applications as stairwell enclosures and corridors? (176)

A. Special

B. Swinging

C. Rolling steel

D. Horizontal sliding

5

Crossword Puzzle

BUILDING CONSTRUCTION RELATED TO THE FIRE SERVICE COURSE WORKBOOK

Across

6 Solid materials used to prevent or limit the vertical and horizontal spread of fire and the products of combustion.

7 Fire barrier that extends from one floor to the bottom of the floor above or to the underside of a fire-rated ceiling assembly.

8 Nonbearing exterior wall attached to the outside of a building with a rigid steel frame.

9 Numerical rating assigned to a material based on the speed and extent to which flame travels over its surface.

11 Unofficial name for the test used to determine the flame spread rating of various materials.

14 Any substance, except plain water, that is applied to another material or substance to reduce the flammability of fuels.

15 Assemblies of building components required by code to have a minimum fire-resistance rating from an independent testing agency.

Down

1 Series of barriers designed to keep flames, smoke, and heat from spreading from one room or floor to another.

2 Exposed interior surfaces of buildings

3 Glass or thermoplastic panel in a window that allows light to pass.

4 Installed to prevent fire spread by automatically closing and covering a doorway in a fire wall during a fire to block the spread of fire through the opening.

5 Ability of substance to vaporize easily at a relatively low temperature.

6 Built of fire resistance materials and usually extending from the foundation up to and through the roof of a building.

10 Having occupants remaining in a structure or vehicle in order to provide protection from a rapidly approaching hazard.

12 Total amount of heat produced or released to the atmosphere.

13 Ability of a substance to do harm within the body.

Chapter 6

Foundations

Write the definition of the terms below on the blanks provided.

1. Strata (184)_____

_____

2. Footing (185) _____

_____

3. Column Footing (186) _____

_____

4. Grillage Footing (186)_____

_____

5. Mat Foundation (186)_____

_____

6. Floating Foundation (187)_____

_____

7. Piles (187) _____

_____

8. Pier (187)_____

_____

9. Underpinning (191) _____

_____

10. Shoring (191) _____

_____

True/False

Write True or False on the blanks provided; if False, write the correct statement on the lines provided.

_____ 1. The type of foundation required for a project depends on the type of climate at the site. (184)

_____

_____

_____ 2. A wall footing is a continuous strip of concrete that supports a wall. (185)

_____

_____

_____ 3. A mat foundation differs from a simple floor slab in its thickness and amount of reinforcement. (186)

_____

_____

_____ 4. A column footing consists of layers of beams placed at right angles to each other that are usually encased in concrete. (186)

_____

_____

_____ 5. A wall foundation is the same as a mat foundation except that it is located beneath a building at a depth such that the weight of soil removed is equal to the weight of the building. (187)

_____

_____

_____ 6. When a pier is designed with a footing, it is known as a belled pier. (187)

_____

_____

_____ 7. Stone is the material most commonly used for foundation walls. (189)

_____

_____

_____ 8. Concrete block basement walls are found only in older buildings. (189)

_____

_____

_____ 9. Expanded polystyrene (EPS) conserves heat in cold climates and reduces the energy needed for air conditioning in warm climates. (190)

_____

_____

_____ 10. Shoring an existing structure is frequently necessary to support a structure until underpinning can be put into place. (191)

_____

_____

Short Answer

Write the correct answers on the blanks provided.

1. What are the factors that determine the type of foundation to be used for a building? (185)

    _____

    _____

    _____

    _____

2. What are the different forms of wall footings? (185)

    _____

    _____

3. List the conditions that lead to settlement of a foundation. (191)

    _____

    _____

    _____

    _____

4. What causes the need for underpinning? (191)

    _____

    _____

    _____

Identification

Write the correct answers on the blanks provided.

1. Identify the piles and piers. (188)

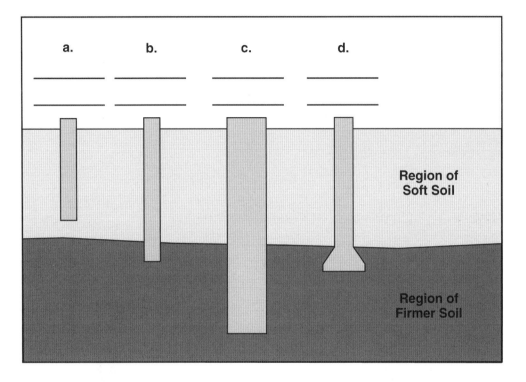

2. Identify the types of foundation walls. (189)

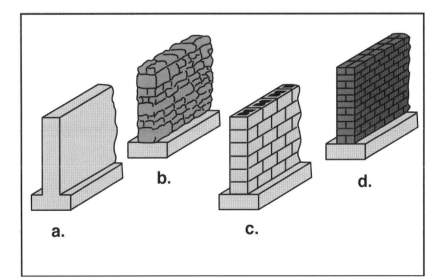

a. _____

b. _____

c. _____

d. _____

3. Identify the two types of settlement. (190)

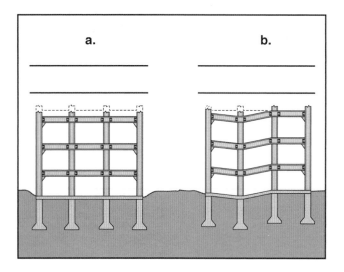

4. Identify the two techniques for supporting an existing wall. (191)

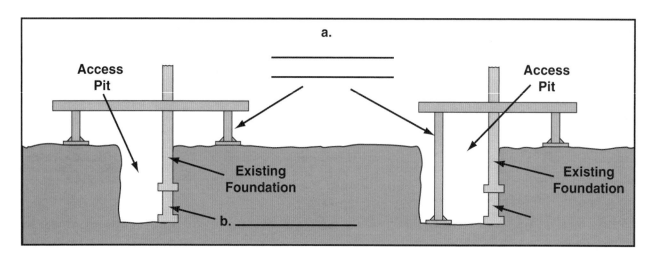

Multiple Choice

Write the correct answers on the blanks provided.

_____ 1. A foundation to a high-rise building requires a foundation that extends ___ feet (m) into the ground. (184)
  A. 25 (7.6)   C. 100 (30)
  B. 50 (15)   D. 150 (45)

_____ 2. Which of the following is a widened base at the bottom of a column or foundation wall? (185)
  A. Pier
  B. Pile
  C. Strata
  D. Footing

_____ 3. Which of the following is a square pad of concrete that supports a column? (186)
  A. Column footing
  B. Grillage footing
  C. Mat foundation
  D. Floating foundation

_____ 4. Which of the following is a thick slab beneath the entire area of a building? (186)
  A. Column footing
  B. Grillage footing
  C. Mat foundation
  D. Floating foundation

_____ 5. Where soil strength is low, a type of foundation known as a ___ foundation may be used. (187)
  A. mat
  B. grillage
  C. column
  D. floating

_____ 6. Which of the following develop load-carrying ability either through friction with the surrounding soil or by being driven into contact with rock or a load-bearing soil layer? (187)

    A. Piers

    B. Piles

    C. Footings

    D. Footer plates

_____ 7. Which of the following is constructed by drilling or digging a shaft and then filling it with concrete? (187)

    A. Piers   C. Footings

    B. Piles   D. Footer plates

_____ 8. Which of the following is the process of strengthening an existing foundation with permanent supports? (191)

    A. Leveling

    B. Shoring

    C. Underpinning

    D. Floating the foundation

Crossword Puzzle

Across

3 Driven into the ground and develop their load-carrying ability either through friction with the surrounding soil.

5 Load-supporting member constructed by drilling or digging a shaft, then filling the shaft with concrete.

7 Footing consisting of layers of beams placed at right angles to each other and usually encased in concrete.

9 Thick slab beneath the entire area of a building.

Down

1 Process of strengthening an existing foundation.

2 Foundation for which the volume of earth excavated will approximately equal the weight of the building supported.

4 Temporary support for formwork or structural components or used to hold sheeting against trench walls.

6 Square pad of concrete that supports a column.

8 Identifiable layers of different soils.

Chapter 7

Wood Construction

Terms

Write the definition of the terms below on the blanks provided.

1. Lumber (198) _____

_____

2. Glulam (199) _____

_____

3. Veneer (201) _____

_____

4. Plywood (201) _____

_____

5. Oriented Strand Board (OSB) (202) _____

_____

6. Composite Panels (202) _____

_____

7. Gusset Plates (204) _____

_____

8. Pyrolysis (208) _____

_____

9. Ambient Temperature (208) _____

_____

10. Heat of Combustion (208) _____

_____

11. Surface-To-Mass Ratio (209) _____

_____

12. Fire Retardant (210) _____

_____

13. Mortise (214) _____

_____

14. Tenon (214) _____

_____

15. Balloon-Frame Construction (216) _____

_____

16. Platform Frame Construction (218) _____

_____

17. Fire Stop (219)_____

_____

18. Draft Stops (220) _____

_____

19. Sheathing (220) _____

_____

True/False

Write True or False on the blanks provided; if False, write the correct statement on the lines provided.

_____ 1. The strength of wood varies significantly with species, grade, and direction of load with respect to the grain. (198)

_____

_____

_____ 2. Wood is stronger in a direction against the grain. (198)

_____

_____

_____ 3. Lumber sizes are typically given in nominal dimensions. (199)

_____

_____

_____ 4. An advantage to producing laminated structural members is that sizes and shapes can be produced that are not available from solid pieces cut from logs. (199)

_____

_____

_____ 5. Plywood is produced in standard sheets measuring 5 feet by 9 feet (1.52 m x 2.74 m). (201)

_____

_____

_____ 6. A grade stamp appears on the back of a structural panel that indicates its intended structural application and its suitability for exposure to water. (202)

_____

_____

_____ 7. Wood trusses are sometimes categorized as light-frame trusses, heavy timber, or split-ring trusses. (204)

_____

_____

_____ 8. Light-frame trusses are made up of members up to 8 or 10 inches (200 mm to 250 mm) long. (205)

_____

_____

_____ 9. Wood box beams are frequently used for floor joists. (206)

_____

_____

_____ 10. Materials with relatively high ignition temperatures are easier to ignite than materials with low ignition temperatures. (207)

_____

_____

_____ 11. The heat of combustion is measured in British Thermal Units (BTU) per pound or kilojoules per kilogram (kj/kg). (208)

_____

_____

_____ 12. A smaller surface area for a given mass of wood permits an overall greater rate of burning. (209)

_____

_____

_____ 13. The slender pieces of structural lumber used in light framing are consumed and fail much more quickly than heavy timbers. (209)

_____

_____

_____ 14. In light wood-frame design, the basic structural support is provided by a framework of beams and columns that are made of wooden timbers. (212)

_____

_____

_____ 15. Older timber construction made use of a type of joint known as a mortise-and-tenon joint. (214)

_____

_____

_____ 16. The most popular form of wood framing is known as post and beam frame construction. (216)

_____

_____

_____ 17. Light wood-frame construction evolved in the 19th century when the development of the sawmill made it possible to expeditiously cut boards from logs. (216)

_____

_____

_____ 18. Post and beam framing is a form of wood-frame construction in which the columns and the beams are of dimensions less than those used in heavy-timber framing but greater than those used in light-frame construction. (215)

_____

_____

_____ 19. The term platform frame construction came from the fragile appearance of the thin, closely spaced studs compared to the massive members used in the earlier timber construction. (216)

_____ 20. The vertical combustible spaces between the studs in platform-frame construction provide a channel for the rapid communication of fire from floor to floor. (217)

_____ 21. From a construction standpoint, balloon-frame buildings are easier to erect than platform-frame buildings. (218)

_____ 22. Platform framing is more prone to shrinkage than balloon-frame buildings, because platform framing makes use of more horizontal members in its frame than a balloon-frame building. (218)

_____ 23. Building codes require draft stopping in the attic spaces of combustible construction. (219)

_____ 24. A layer of building paper is provided between the sheathing and the siding to act as a vapor barrier. (220)

_____ 25. Gypsum board is not often used in modern construction because it is relatively labor intensive. (223)

_____

_____

_____ 26. When wood-frame construction framing members become exposed to a fire, rapid failure of the structural systems must be anticipated. (224)

_____

_____

Short Answer

Write the correct answers on the blanks provided.

1. List three wood products that are available for use in the construction industry. (198)

_____

_____

_____

2. List the wood panel products. (201)

_____

_____

_____

3. List the nonveneered products. (202)

_____

_____

_____

4. What are the variables that affect the ignition temperature of wood? (207)

_____

_____

_____

_____

_____

_____

5. What are the chemicals used in a fire-retardant treatment? (210)

_____

_____

_____

_____

_____

_____

6. List the factors engineers must take into account when designing connections for heavy-timber construction. (214)

_____

_____

_____

_____

7. List locations where firestopping is required. (219)

_____

_____

_____

_____

_____

8. List the material that is included in exterior walls of a wood-frame building. (220-222)

_____

_____

_____

_____

_____

Identification

Write the correct answers on the blanks provided.

1. Identify the information on the fire-retardant treated wood label. (211)

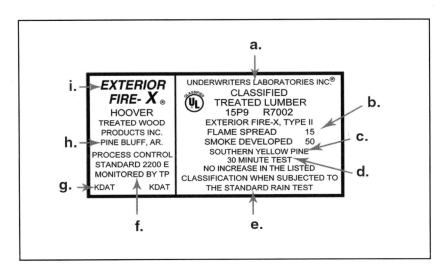

a. _____

b. _____

c. _____

d. _____

e. _____

f. _____

g. _____

h. _____

i. _____

2. Identify the components of balloon-frame construction. (217)

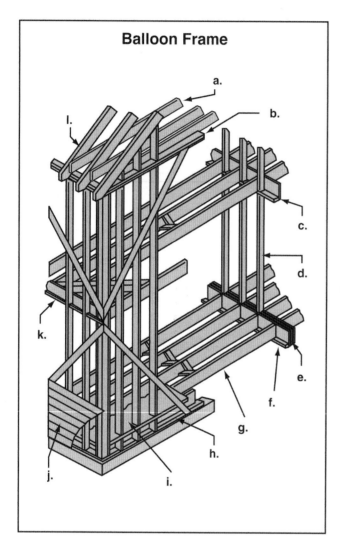

Balloon Frame

a. _____

b. _____

c. _____

d. _____

e. _____

f. _____

g. _____

h. _____

i. _____

j. _____

k. _____

l. _____

3. Identify the components of platform-frame construction. (217)

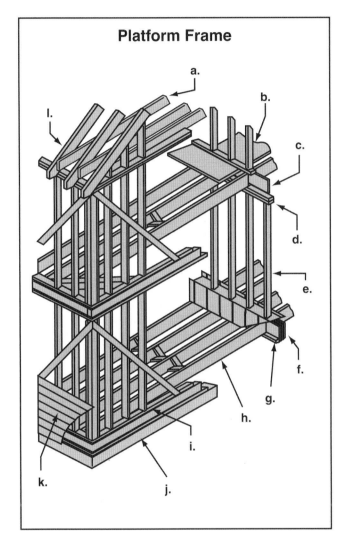

Platform Frame

a. _____

b. _____

c. _____

d. _____

e. _____

f. _____

g. _____

h. _____

i. _____

j. _____

k. _____

l. _____

4. Identify the components of a wall in platform-frame construction. (219)

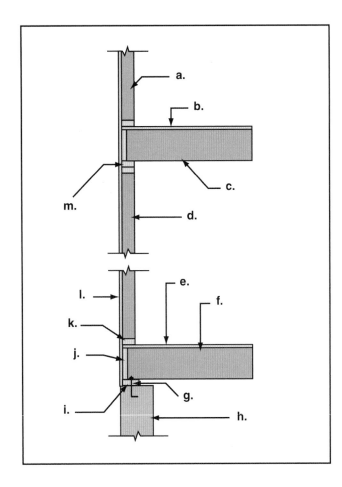

a. _____

b. _____

c. _____

d. _____

e. _____

f. _____

g. _____

h. _____

i. _____

j. _____

k. _____

l. _____

m. _____

Multiple Choice

Write the correct answers on the blanks provided.

_____ 1. Which of the following includes boards, dimension lumber, and timber? (199)
  A. Panel
  B. Solid lumber
  C. Laminated wood
  D. Manufactured component

_____ 2. Which of the following members are produced by joining flat strips of wood with glue? (199)
  A. Panel   C. Laminated wood
  B. Solid lumber   D. Manufactured component

_____ 3. Which of the following new products allows the use of the outer fibers of a log as well as the inner portions traditionally used? (201)
   A. Panel
   B. Solid lumber
   C. Laminated wood
   D. Structural composite lumber

_____ 4. Which of the following is made up of several thin layers or veneer that are rotary sliced from rotating logs and glued together? (201)
   A. Plywood
   B. Waferboard
   C. Particleboard
   D. Oriented strand board

_____ 5. Which of the following uses long, strand-like wood particles that are compressed and glued into three to five layers? (202)
   A. Plywood
   B. Waferboard
   C. Particleboard
   D. Oriented strand board

_____ 6. Which of the following is made from wood particles bonded with synthetic resins under heat and pressure? (202)
   A. Plywood
   B. Waferboard
   C. Particleboard
   D. Oriented strand board

_____ 7. Which of the following uses wafer-like pieces of wood? (202)
   A. Plywood
   B. Waferboard
   C. Particleboard
   D. Oriented strand board

_____ 8. Which of the following trusses makes use of a short circular piece of steel within and between two adjacent wood members to transfer the load between the members? (205)
   A. Metal
   B. Split-ring
   C. Light-frame
   D. Heavy timber

_____ 9. Which of the following is the thermal decomposition of wood and begins at a temperature somewhere below approximately 392°F (200°C)? (208)
   A. Pyrolysis
   B. Heat of combustion
   C. Ignition temperature
   D. Ambient temperature

_____ 10. The ___ of a fuel is the total amount of thermal energy that could be released if the fuel were completely burned. (208)
   A. pyrolysis
   B. heat of combustion
   C. ignition temperature
   D. ambient temperature

_____ 11. Which of the following is a wood-like product produced from wood fiber and polyethylene or polyvinylchloride (PVC)? (211)
   A. Veneer
   B. Particle board
   C. Exterior gypsum sheathing
   D. Thermoplastic composite lumber

_____ 12. Which of the following evolved from hand-hewn wooden timbers that were painstakingly cut from logs? (212)
   A. Balloon framing
   B. Platform framing
   C. Heavy-timber framing
   D. Post and beam framing

_____ 13. In ___ frame construction, the exterior wall studs are continuous from the foundation to the roof. (216)

    A. balloon

    B. platform

    C. heavy-timber

    D. post and beam

_____ 14. In ___ framing, the exertior wall vertical studs are not continuous to the second floor. (218)

    A. balloon

    B. platform

    C. heavy-timber

    D. post and beam

_____ 15. Which of the following is installed on the outside of the studs to provide structural stability? (220)

    A. Siding

    B. Sheathing

    C. Insulation

    D. Building paper

_____ 16. Which of the following provides the exterior cladding of a wood-frame building? (222)

    A. Siding

    B. Sheathing

    C. Insulation

    D. Building paper

_____ 17. Wood-frame buildings with interior walls exposed with no interior finish are classified as Type: (223)

    A. V-A construction.

    B. V-B construction.

    C. IV-A construction.

    D. IV-B construction.

_____ 18. Which of the following types of construction is intended to decrease the vulnerability of structures to exposure from wildland fires? (226)

    A. Brick veneer

    B. Wood-frame

    C. Fire-resistive

    D. Ignition-resistive

7

Crossword Puzzle

Across

5 Solid materials, such as wood blocks, used to prevent or limit the vertical and horizontal spread of fire and the products of combustion.

7 Construction material made of many small wooden pieces (strands) bonded together to form sheets, similar to plywood.

9 Thermal or chemical decomposition of fuel (matter) because of heat that generally results in the lowered ignition temperature of the material.

11 Temperature of the surrounding environment.

12 Type of framing in which each floor is built as a separate platform and the studs are not continuous beyond each floor.

14 Notch, hole, or space cut into a piece of timber to receive the projecting part (tenon) of another piece of timber.

15 Metal or wooden plates used to connect and strengthen the intersections of metal or wooden truss components.

17 Total amount of thermal energy (heat) that could be generated by the combustion (oxidation) reaction if a fuel were completely burned.

18 Type of structural framing used in some single-story and multistory wood frame buildings wherein the studs are continuous from the foundation to the roof.

Down

1 Wood sheet product made from several thin veneer layers that are sliced from logs and glued together.

2 Surface layer of attractive material laid over a base of common material.

3 Covering applied to the framing of a building to which siding is applied.

4 Dividers hung from the ceiling in large open areas that are designed to minimize the mushrooming effect of heat and smoke.

5 Material or substance and that is designed to reduce the flammability of fuels or slow their rate of combustion by chemical or physical action.

6 Produced with parallel external face veneers bonded to a core of reconstituted fibers.

8 Short for glue-laminated structural lumber.

10 The ratio of the surface area of the fuel to the mass of the fuel.

13 Lengths of wood cut and prepared for use in construction.

16 Projecting member in a piece of wood or other material for insertion into a mortise to make a joint.

Chapter 8

Masonry and Ordinary Construction

Terms

Write the definition of the terms below on the blanks provided.

1. Course (235) _____

_____

2. Header Course (235) _____

_____

3. Concrete Block (235) _____

_____

4. Mortar (236) _____

_____

5. Portland Cement (237) _____

_____

6. Bearing Wall (237) _____

_____

7. Wythe (239) _____

_____

8. Lintel (241) _____

_____

9. Parapet (243) _____

_____

10. Fire Cut (245) _____

_____

11. Fascia (250) _____

_____

True/False

Write True or False on the blanks provided; if False, write the correct statement on the lines provided.

_____   1. Masonry remains a commonly used construction material today and many different types of buildings are constructed using masonry. (233)

_____

_____

_____   2. The hardness of a concrete block is dependent on the soil used in its composition. (234)

_____

_____

_____   3. Concrete blocks are also known as concrete masonry units (CMUs). (235)

_____

_____

_____   4. Masonry units have significant tensile strength. (236)

_____

_____

_____ 5. Most mortar is produced from a mixture of portland cement, hydrated lime, sand, and water. (237)

_____

_____

_____ 6. Sand-lime mortar was commonly used in masonry construction until the 1990's. (237)

_____

_____

_____ 7. Masonry walls are found in both fire-resistive and non-fire-resistive buildings. (238)

_____

_____

_____ 8. In the case of a cavity wall, the placement of metal ties is especially important because the use of a brick header course usually is not practical. (240)

_____

_____

_____ 9. Cavity walls can be reinforced by placing vertical steel rods in a cavity between two adjacent wythes of a brick wall. (240)

_____

_____

_____ 10. In older multistory buildings, interior load-bearing masonry walls were used to enclose stairwells or elevator shafts. (240)

_____

_____

_____ 11. The purpose of a parapet on an exterior wall can be both architectural and functional. (243)

_____

_____

_____ 12. Wood-frame construction is also known as "masonry, wood-joisted " construction. (244)

_____

_____

_____ 13. The purpose of a fire cut is to allow the beam to fall away freely from a wall in case of structural collapse. (245)

_____

_____

_____ 14. A masonry wall, 18 inches (450 mm) thick, will have an inherently low degree of fire resistance. (246)

_____

_____

_____ 15. A mansard-style fascia forms a projection beyond the building wall that creates a concealed space through which a fire can communicate. (250)

_____

_____

Short Answer

Write the correct answers on the blanks provided.

1. List the materials used to construct masonry units. (234)

_____

_____

_____

_____

_____

_____

2. List the major advantage in mill construction from a firefighter's standpoint. (252)

_____

_____

_____

Identification

Write the correct answers on the blanks provided.

1. Identify the components of the masonry wall. (240)

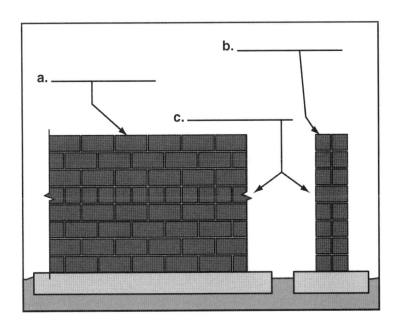

2. Identify the opening in the masonry wall. (241)

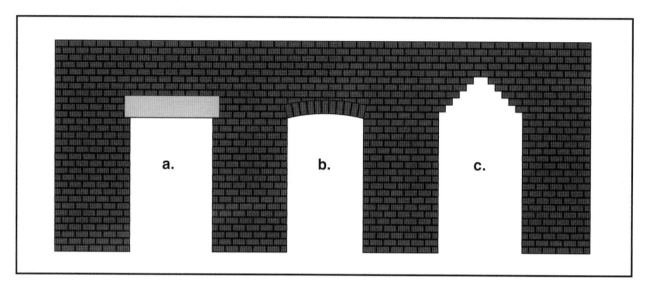

a. ————————————————

b. ————————————————

c. ————————————————

3. Identify the components of a tie rod that reinforce a masonry wall. (248)

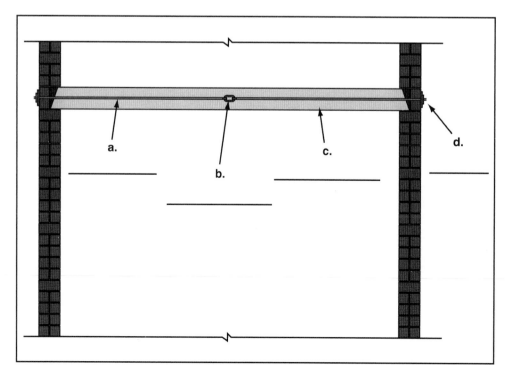

Multiple Choice

Write the correct answers on the blanks provided.

_____ 1. Which of the following are produced from a variety of locally available clays and shales? (234)
A. Bricks
B. Stones
C. Gypsum blocks
D. Concrete blocks

_____ 2. Which of the following consist of pieces of rock that have been removed from a quarry and cut to the size and shape desired? (235)
A. Bricks
B. Stones
C. Gypsum blocks
D. Concrete blocks

_____ 3. Which of the following has the primary function of bonding the individual masonry units into a solid mass? (236)
A. Grout
B. Mortar
C. Cement
D. Caulking

_____ 4. When a masonry wall is constructed, the masonry units are laid side by side in a horizontal layer known as a: (239)
A. lintel.
B. wythe.
C. course.
D. parapet.

_____ 5. When bricks are placed end-to-end, they create a: (240)
A. cavity wall.
B. soldier course.
C. header course.
D. stretcher course.

_____ 6. Bricks placed vertically on end are called a: (240)
   A. cavity wall.
   B. soldier course.
   C. header course.
   D. stretcher course.

_____ 7. Which of the following is a course of bricks across two wythes with ends of the bricks facing out? (240)
   A. Cavity wall
   B. Soldier course
   C. Header course
   D. Stretcher course

_____ 8. Which of the following is a beam over an opening in a masonry wall? (241)
   A. Lintel   C. Course
   B. Wythe   D. Parapet

_____ 9. Which of the following is an extension of a masonry or steel wall that protects above the roof? (243)
   A. Lintel   C. Course
   B. Wythe   D. Parapet

_____ 10. Buildings with masonry exterior walls and wood joisted interior framing are classified as ___ construction in the building codes. (246)
   A. Type I   C. Type III
   B. Type II   D. Type IV

_____ 11. Mill construction is commonly known as ___ construction. (250)
   A. wood-frame
   B. heavy-timber
   C. fire-resistant
   D. post and beam

_____ 12. In building codes, mill construction is classified as Type ___ construction. (250)
   A. I
   B. II
   C. III
   D. IV

Crossword Puzzle

Across

3 Angled cut made at the end of a wood joist or wood beam that rests in a masonry wall.

4 Portion of the exterior walls of a building that extends above the roof.

6 Also known as concrete masonry units (CMU).

8 Support for masonry over an opening; usually made of steel angles or other rolled shapes singularly or in combination.

9 Cement-like liquid material that hardens and bonds individual masonry units into a solid mass.

10 Flat horizontal or vertical board located at the outer face of a cornice.

Down

1 Single vertical row of multiple rows of masonry units in a wall, usually brick.

2 Wall that supports itself and the weight of the roof and/or other internal structural framing components such as the floor beams above it.

5 Most commonly used cement consisting chiefly of calcium and aluminum silicates.

7 Course of bricks with the ends of the bricks facing outward.

Chapter 9

Steel Construction

Terms

Write the definition of the terms below on the blanks provided.

1. Ductile (258) _____

   _____

2. Girder (262) _____

   _____

3. Bar Joist (265) _____

   _____

4. Gusset Plates (271)_____

   _____

5. Gypsum Board (272) _____

   _____

6. Cementitious (273)_____

   _____

7. Intumescent Coating (274) _____

   _____

8. Membrane Ceiling (274) _____

   _____

9

Write True or False on the blanks provided; if False, write the correct statement on the lines provided.

_____ 1. A firefighter must understand that the behavior of steel under fire conditions depends on the mass of the steel and the degree of fire resistance provided. (258)

_____

_____

_____ 2. The higher carbon content of steel compared to that of cast iron results in a material that is ductile rather than brittle. (258)

_____

_____

_____ 3. Cold-rolled steel is used for members that have a thin cross-section, such as floor and roof decking and wall studs. (258)

_____

_____

_____ 4. To the fire service, the deterioration of the strength of steel at elevated temperatures is its most significant characteristic. (259)

_____

_____

_____ 5. When higher stresses exist in the steel, it must be heated to a higher temperature for the yield point to be reached. (260)

_____

_____

_____ 6. Welding beams and columns in steel-frame buildings was used in the first half of the 20th century but is not practical to use today. (262)

_____

_____

_____ 7. Bar joists are frequently used in closely spaced configurations for the support of floors or roof decks. (266)

_____

_____

_____ 8. Gable roof simple-frame structures must be braced diagonally to prevent deflections on the direction perpendicular to the plane of the frame sections. (267)

_____

_____

_____ 9. The strength of steel is such that it can be used in very slender forms such as rods and cables. (268)

_____

_____

_____ 10. The lower the numerical valve of the slenderness ratio of a steel column, the more likely that buckling will occur. (269)

_____

_____

_____ 11. Open-web joists cannot be used to support precast concrete panels or wood decking. (270)

_____

_____

_____ 12. The greater the mass of a steel member, the less likely it will fail in a fire. (270)

_____

_____

_____ 13. The simple connections used in the beam and girder type of frame have a greater mass of steel at the point of connection than do rigid connections. (270)

_____

_____

_____ 14. Under fire conditions, unprotected light-gauge steel sheeting may fail structurally although it will not melt. (272)

_____

_____

_____ 15. A very commonly used method of protecting a steel floor or roof assembly is the membrane ceiling. (274)

_____

_____

Short Answer

Write the correct answers on the blanks provided.

1. What are the basic properties of steel? (258)

_____

_____

_____

_____

_____

2. What are the disadvantages steel possesses? (259)

_____

_____

3. List the factors in which the speed of unprotected steel fails when exposed to a fire. (260)

_____

_____

_____

_____

_____

4. How are beams and columns in steel-frame buildings connected? (262)

_____

_____

5. What are the classifications of beam and girder steel frames? (263)

_____

_____

_____

6. List the three methods by which steel structural members can be used to support floors in multistory buildings. (270)

_____

_____

_____

Multiple Choice

Write the correct answers on the blanks provided.

_____ 1. When a framing system is classified as a ___ frame, the connections between the beams and the columns are designed to resist bending forces. (264)
   A. truss   C. simple
   B. rigid   D. semi-rigid

_____ 2. In the case of a ___ frame, the joints are designed primarily to support a vertical force. (264)
   A. truss
   B. rigid
   C. simple
   D. semi-rigid

_____ 3. In a ___ frame, the connections are not completely rigid but possess enough rigidity to provide some diagonal support to the structure. (264)
   A. truss
   B. rigid
   C. simple
   D. semi-rigid

_____ 4. Which of the following is the top of the rigid frame? (267)
   A. Arch
   B. Knee
   C. Crown
   D. Elbow

_____ 5. Which of the following is the point where inclined members of a rigid frame intersect the vertical members? (267)
   A. Arch
   B. Knee
   C. Crown
   D. Elbow

_____ 6. Which of the following is constructed as a solid arch that may be built up from angles and webs with a cross section similar to that of a beam? (267)
   A. Girder arch
   B. Crown arch
   C. Simple arch
   D. Trussed arch

_____ 7. Which of the following is a number that compares the unbraced length of a column to the shape and area of its cross-section? (269)
   A. Buckling ratio   C. Cross-section ratio
   B. Slenderness ratio   D. Rigid strength ratio

8. Which of the following strengthens steel connections and increases the steel mass at the connection, thereby decreasing its possibility of failure? (271)

   A. Rivet

   B. Knee joint

   C. Truss plate

   D. Gusset plate

9. In a gabled rigid-frame structure, the ___ between the roof and the wall will be the strongest part of the frame and the last part to fail. (271)

   A. rivets

   B. knee joint

   C. truss plate

   D. gusset plate

10. Which of the following can be used as an insulating material either in the form of flat boards or a plaster? (272)

    A. Gypsum

    B. Mineral tile

    C. Intumescent material

    D. Cementitious material

11. Which of the following is a mineral fiber or expanded aggregate coating such as vermiculite or perlite? (273)

    A. Gypsum

    B. Mineral tile

    C. Intumescent material

    D. Spray-applied fire-resistive material

12. Which of the following undergoes a chemical reaction and will char, foam, and expand when heated? (274)

    A. Gypsum

    B. Mineral tile

    C. Intumescent material

    D. Spray-applied fire-resistive material

9

Crossword Puzzle

Across

5 Capable of being shaped, bent, or drawn out.

6 Coating or paintlike product that expands when exposed to the heat of a fire.

7 Usually refers to a suspended, insulating ceiling tile system.

Down

1 Metal or wooden plates used to connect and strengthen the intersections of metal or wooden truss components.

2 Open web truss constructed entirely of steel, with steel bars used as the web members.

3 Containing or composed of cement.

4 Widely used interior finish material.

8 Large, horizontal structural member used to support joists and beams at isolated points along their length.

Chapter 10

Concrete Construction

Write the definition of the terms below on the blanks provided.

1. Aggregate (281) _____
   _____

2. Curing (282) _____
   _____

3. Heat of Hydration (282) _____
   _____

4. Admixture (283) _____
   _____

5. Pretensioned Reinforcing (286) _____
   _____

6. Post-Tensioned Reinforcing (286) _____
   _____

7. Cast-in-Place Concrete (288) _____
   _____

8. Precast Concrete (291) _____
   _____

9. Tilt-Up Construction (293) _____
   _____

10

10. Curtain Wall (295) _____

_____

11. Spalling (297) _____

_____

Write True or False on the blanks provided; if False, write the correct statement on the lines provided.

_____ 1. Improper curing methods will negatively affect the finished surface of concrete as well as its strength. (282)

_____

_____

_____ 2. Concrete initially hardens fairly slowly but then begins to harden more quickly. (282)

_____

_____

_____ 3. Concrete that is cured at or above 100°F (37°C) will not reach its proper strength. (283)

_____

_____

_____ 4. Like masonry, concrete is weaker in compression but stronger in tension. (284)

_____

_____

_____ 5. With ordinary reinforcing, steel bars are placed in the formwork and the wet concrete is placed in the formwork around the bars. (284)

_____

_____

_____ 6. The primary function of placing reinforcing steel in concrete is to resist compressive forces. (284)

_____

_____

_____ 7. The single most important factor in determining the ultimate strength of concrete is the water-to-cement ratio. (288)

_____

_____

_____ 8. Concrete buildings are constructed with structural systems that use bearing walls formed from precast concrete. (290)

_____

_____

_____ 9. A poured concrete slab can be supported by structural steel beams instead of concrete beams. (291)

_____

_____

_____ 10. A major disadvantage to using precast concrete is the need to transport the finished components to the job site where it increases costs and limits the size of the shapes that can be precast. (293)

_____

_____

_____ 11. A common form of construction used with precast concrete is known as flat plate construction. (293)

_____

_____

_____ 12. When precast beams are to be supported by columns, the beams may be supported by corbels cast into the columns. (294)

_____

_____

_____ 13. A very common application of cast-in-place concrete is in the construction of parking garages. (294)

_____

_____

_____ 14. Prestressed concrete systems may be somewhat more vulnerable to failure than ordinary reinforced concrete. (295)

_____

_____

_____ 15. Concrete tends to retain the heat of an exposing fire and release it slowly, similar to the manner in which a masonry oven releases heat. (297)

_____

_____

Short Answer

Write the correct answers on the blanks provided.

1. List the different types of concrete. (283)

    _____

    _____

    _____

    _____

    _____

    _____

    _____

2. What are the techniques used to reinforce concrete? (284)

    _____

    _____

    _____

3. List the common cast-in-place structural systems. (290)

    _____

    _____

4. List the advantages to using precast concrete. (292)

    _____

    _____

    _____

    _____

5. List the variables that affect fire resistance of a concrete assembly. (296)

    _____

    _____

    _____

    _____

    _____

Multiple Choice

Write the correct answers on the blanks provided.

_____ 1. Hardening of concrete involves a chemical process known as: (282)
A. hydration.
B. precasting.
C. reinforcement.
D. underpinning.

_____ 2. Concrete that is curing must be maintained at the correct temperature, ideally between: (283)
A. 32° to 48°F (0°C to 8°C).
B. 50° to 70°F (10°C to 21°C).
C. 75° to 98°F (24°C to 36°C).
D. 100° to 115°F (37°C to 46°C).

_____ 3. Vertical reinforcing bars are known as ___ and are provided to resist the diagonal tension. (284)
A. stirrups
B. knee joints
C. gusset plates
D. reinforcing brackets

_____ 4. In which of the following are steel strands stretched between anchors producing a tensile force in the steel? (286)
A. Casting
B. Spalling
C. Pretensioning
D. Posttensioning

_____ 5. When concrete is ___, the reinforcing steel is not tensioned until after the concrete has hardened. (286)
A. casted
B. spalled
C. pretensioned
D. posttensioned

6. Which of the following is concrete placed into forms at the building site as a wet mass that hardens in the forms? (288)

A. Precast

B. Pretensioned

C. Posttensioned

D. Cast-in-place

7. Which of the following is concrete placed in forms and cured at a plant away from the job site? (288)

A. Precast

B. Pretensioned

C. Posttensioned

D. Cast-in-place

8. Which of the following tests is used to check the moisture content of concrete by measuring the amount that a small, cone-shaped sample of the concrete settles after it is removed from a standard-sized test mold? (289)

A. Slump

B. Tension

C. Compression

D. Reinforcement

9. Which of the following concrete tests is accurate but has the disadvantage of requiring that the concrete be permitted to harden before the results are known? (289)

A. Slump

B. Tension

C. Compression

D. Reinforcement

10. Which of the following frames is a simple system that consists of a concrete slab supported by concrete columns? (290)

A. Waffle

B. Precast

C. Slab and beam

D. Flat-slab concrete

_____ 11. Which of the following framing systems is extremely lightweight and is best suited for a building with light floor loads? (290)
   A. Waffle
   B. Precast
   C. Slab and beam
   D. Flat-slab concrete

_____ 12. Which of the following provides a thicker slab while eliminating the weight of unnecessary concrete in the bottom half of the slab? (291)
   A. Waffle construction
   B. Precast construction
   C. Slab and beam construction
   D. Flat-slab concrete construction

_____ 13. Prestressed concrete systems can yield vulnerability to failure at a temperature of around: (295)
   A. 250°F (121°C).
   B. 372°F (189°C).
   C. 752°F (400°C).
   D. 950°F (510°C).

_____ 14. Which of the following is caused primarily by the expansion of the excess moisture within the concrete when it is either heated or when it freezes? (297)
   A. Casting
   B. Spalling
   C. Shoring
   D. Heat sinking

_____ 15. The extent to which concrete undergoes spalling depends on the: (297)
   A. time of day.
   B. types of aggregates in the concrete.
   C. humidity in the air at time of placing.
   D. amount of excess moisture in the concrete.

_____ 16. Concrete ___ heat when it is exposed to a fire. (297)
   A. absorbs
   B. deflects
   C. radiates
   D. redirects

17. Spalling ___ concrete structurally. (297)
    A. shortens
    B. elongates
    C. weakens
    D. strengthens

18. New concrete that is not completely cured is subject to ___ spalling when exposed to a fire. (297)
    A. less severe
    B. more severe
    C. a longer time of
    D. the same amount of

Crossword Puzzle

Across

1 During the hardening of concrete, heat is given off by the chemical process of hydration.

4 Gravel, stone, sand, or other inert materials used in concrete.

6 Method of building construction where the concrete building member is poured and set according to specification in a controlled environment.

7 Refers to concrete that is poured into forms as a liquid and assumes the shape of the form in the position and location it will be used.

9 Reinforcing steel in the concrete is tensioned after the concrete has hardened.

10 Expansion of excess moisture within concrete due to exposure to the heat of a fire resulting in tensile forces within the concrete.

Down

2 Ingredients or chemicals added to concrete mix to produce concrete with specific characteristics.

3 Steel strands are stretched between anchors producing a tensile force in the steel.

5 Type of construction in which concrete wall sections (slabs) are cast on the concrete floor of the building and are then tilted up into the vertical position.

7 Nonbearing exterior wall attached to the outside of a building with a rigid steel frame.

8 Maintaining conditions to achieve proper strength during the hardening of concrete.

Chapter 11

Roofs

Terms

Write the definition of the terms below on the blanks provided.

1. Shed Roof (306) _____
   _____

2. Gabled Roof (307) _____
   _____

3. Hip Roof (307) _____
   _____

4. Gambrel Roof (307) _____
   _____

5. Mansard Roof (307) _____
   _____

6. Butterfly Roof (307) _____
   _____

7. Monitor Roof (308) _____
   _____

8. Sawtooth Roof (308) _____
   _____

9. Lamella Arch (309) _____
   _____

10. Rafter (314) _____

_____

11. Bowstring Truss (317) _____

_____

12. Roof Covering (320) _____

_____

13. Vapor Barrier (320) _____

_____

14. Membrane Roof (321) _____

_____

15. Wear Course (322) _____

_____

16. Rain Roof (329) _____

_____

17. Penthouse (331) _____

_____

18. Skylights (332) _____

_____

True/False

Write True or False on the blanks provided; if False, write the correct statement on the lines provided.

_____ 1. Flat roofs present a drainage problem. (305)

_____

_____

_____ 2. A butterfly roof slopes in two directions, with a break in the slope on each side. (307)

_____

_____

_____ 3. The lamella arch is a special form of arched roof. (309)

_____

_____

_____ 4. The closed web design of truss joints permits the rapid spread of fire. (311)

_____

_____

_____ 5. Unprotected lightweight open-web joists can be expected to fail quickly in a fire. (311)

_____

_____

_____ 6. Trusses are the inclined joists used to support some types of pitched roofs. (313)

_____

_____

_____ 7. A fink truss is a truss in which all chords and diagonal members lie in the same plane. (315)

_____ 8. Failure of tie rods will permit arches to collapse inward. (317)

_____ 9. Wood planks used for roof decks will have a minimum 1-inch (25 mm) nominal thickness. (318)

_____ 10. A building with wood-joisted floors usually will have a steel-framed roof. (319)

_____ 11. Single-ply membranes are most often made of synthetic rubber. (322)

_____ 12. Roof coverings for pitched roofs are typically shingles, tiles, or metal. (323)

_____ 13. Wood shingles are usually installed over an underlayment. (325)

_____ 14. Asphalt shingles tend to drip and run under fire conditions. (325)

_____

_____

_____ 15. Corrugated roofing sheets are weak and must be installed over roof decking. (327)

_____

_____

_____ 16. A second roof constructed over an existing roof is called a temporary roof. (329)

_____

_____

_____ 17. A rooftop garden constitutes a live load on the roof structural system. (330)

_____

_____

_____ 18. Skylights provide a rapid means of ventilating heat and smoke. (332)

_____

_____

_____ 19. Ceilings usually play a structural role in a building. (333)

_____

_____

_____ 20. It is not uncommon for older buildings to have a new ceiling installed beneath an existing ceiling. (333)

_____

_____

11

Short Answer

Write the correct answers on the blanks provided.

1. What does a roof slope of 3 to 12 designate? (306)

   _____

   _____

2. Upon what does the type of roof covering depend? (319)

   _____

   _____

3. What are the components of a flat roof? (320)

   _____

   _____

   _____

   _____

   _____

4. What are some operational problems of fires involving clay, slate, and cement tiles? (326)

   _____

   _____

   _____

   _____

   _____

5. What are the test procedures contained in NFPA® 256? (328)

   _____

   _____

   _____

   _____

   _____

   _____

Matching

Write the correct answers on the blanks provided.

_____ 1. Thin, tapered slabs of wood sawn from pieces of a tree trunk (324)

_____ 2. Split from the wood either by hand or by machine (324)

_____ 3. Produced from heavy sheets of mineral-impregnated felt made from rag, paper, or wool fiber (324)

_____ 4. Produced from hard rock; can have a life expectancy of 150 years (324)

_____ 5. Dense, hard, and nonabsorbent material and can be used for flat or curved tiles (324)

_____ 6. Made from Portland cement, aggregate, and water; has greater longevity than wood tiles (324)

A. Asphalt shingles
B. Clay tile
C. Concrete tiles
D. Slate
E. Wood shakes
F. Wood shingles

Identification

Write the names of each of the types of pitched roofs on the lines provided. (307)

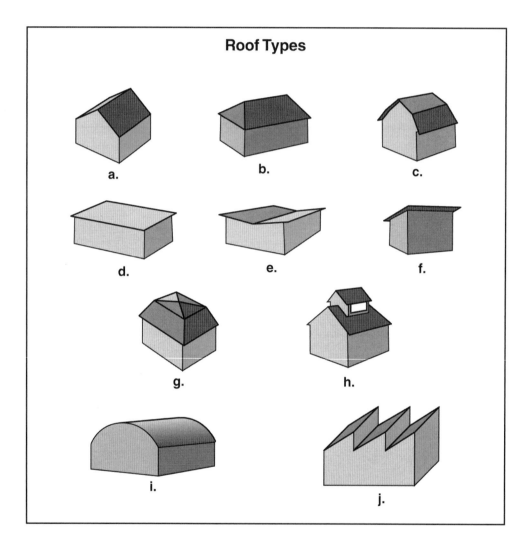

Roof Types

a.

b.

c.

d.

e.

f.

g.

h.

i.

j.

a. _____

b. _____

c. _____

d. _____

e. _____

f. _____

g. _____

h. _____

i. _____

j. _____

Multiple Choice

Write the correct answers on the blanks provided.

_____ 1. Which of the following statements regarding the safety of roofs is MOST accurate? (304)
   A. Roofs are usually stronger than floors.
   B. Roofs are most often made up of one single layer.
   C. Roof construction does not include concealed spaces.
   D. Loads may be added to roofs for which they are not designed.

_____ 2. Which pitched roof consists of two inclined surfaces that meet at their high side to form a ridge? (307)
   A. Hip
   B. Gable
   C. Gambrel
   D. Mansard

_____ 3. A ___ roof is designed to provide light and ventilation. (308)
   A. lantern
   B. monitor
   C. butterfly
   D. sawtooth

_____ 4. What type of roof is created from triangles arranged in three dimensions to form a nearly spherical surface? (310)
   A. Dormers
   B. Domed roof
   C. Lamella arch
   D. Geodesic domes

_____ 5. Which of the following is the BEST indicator that a roof is weakening? (311)
   A. Sagging of roof
   B. Soft or spongy roof conditions
   C. Wood joists losing their strength
   D. Any indication of advanced or heavy fire development

_____ 6. Fireproofing can be omitted from roof supports when the roof is located more than ___ feet (m) above the floor in an assembly occupancy. (312)
A. 10 (3)
B. 15 (4.6)
C. 20 (6.6)
D. 25 (7.6)

_____ 7. Flat roofs must be designed to support the weight of: (312)
A. aerial ladders.
B. a few workers.
C. an entire fire crew.
D. only one worker at a time.

_____ 8. Rafters may be constructed of all of the following EXCEPT: (314)
A. wood.
B. masonry.
C. steel beams.
D. steel trusses.

_____ 9. What makes trusses vulnerable to early failure under fire conditions? (314-315)
A. Release rate of components
B. Independence of components
C. Reduced mass of components
D. Increased mass of components

_____ 10. A ___ truss uses a curved top chord. (316)
A. fink
B. pratt
C. bowstring
D. monoplane

_____ 11. Which type of trusses are most common for pitched roofs? (317)
A. Pratt
B. Bowstring
C. Connected
D. Monoplane

12. Which of the following is the portion of roof construction to which the roof covering is applied? (317)
    A. Roof deck
    B. Roof slabs
    C. Roof planks
    D. Roof sheathing

13. Which of the following is NOT used for construction of roof decks? (318)
    A. Plywood
    B. Wood planks
    C. Galvanized steel
    D. Precast gypsum planks

14. A vapor barrier is needed when the outdoor temperature is below: (320)
    A. 20°F (-7°C).
    B. 30°F (-1°C).
    C. 40°F (5°C).
    D. 50°F (10°C).

15. Which type of membrane roofing uses several overlapping layers of roofing felt saturated with tar or asphalt? (321)
    A. Built-up
    B. Single-ply
    C. Multi-ply
    D. Fluid-applied

16. What is a major difference between flat and pitched roofs? (323)
    A. Water immediately drains from a flat roof.
    B. Water immediately drains from a pitched roof.
    C. Flat roofs rarely have water pooling on the surface.
    D. Flat roofs use the force of gravity to drain water from the roofs.

_____ 17. Which of the following statements regarding wood roof shingles is MOST accurate? (325)

    A. Fire-resistant wood shingles can be identified by their color.

    B. Wood roof shingles are more fire-resistant than asphalt shingles.

    C. Painting fire retardant shingles can increase the effect of the fire retardant.

    D. Wood shingles pressure-impregnated with a fire-retardant solution meet model code requirements.

_____ 18. Which roof coverings are effective against a light fire exposure? (328)

    A. Class A

    B. Class B

    C. Class C

    D. Class D

_____ 19. Which of the following types of roofs involves the use of the roof surface of a building for a rooftop garden? (329)

    A. Green

    B. Garden

    C. Environmental

    D. Energy-efficient

_____ 20. What type of roof produces clean and reliable energy? (330)

    A. Green

    B. Energy

    C. Garden

    D. Photovoltaic

_____ 21. Which of the following statements regarding air-supported roofs is MOST accurate? (331)

    A. Air-supported roofs are easily ventilated.

    B. Air-supported roofs are typically used for warehouses.

    C. The curved roof easily supports the weight of firefighters.

    D. Air-supported roofs do not lend themselves to conventional fire fighting tactics.

_____ 22. Which of the following are small structures erected on the main roof of a building? (331)
   A. Catwalks
   B. Skylights
   C. Penthouses
   D. Garden roofs

Crossword Puzzle

Across

3 A special type of arch constructed of short pieces of wood called lamellas.

6 Roof style similar to an exaggerated lantern roof having a raised section along the ridge line.

9 Inclined beam that supports a roof, runs parallel to the slope of the roof, and to which the roof decking is attached.

11 Style of gabled roof on which each side slopes at two different angles.

12 Roof style characterized by a series of alternating vertical walls and sloping roofs.

14 Pitched roof that has no gables.

15 Style of pitched roof with square ends in which the end walls of the building form triangular areas beneath the roof.

16 Roof covering that consists of a single layer of waterproof synthetic membrane over one or more layers of insulation on a roof deck.

17 Increase natural illumination within buildings in rooms or over stairways and other vertical shafts that extend to the roof.

Down

1 Watertight material used to prevent the passage of moisture or water vapor into and through walls or roofs.

2 Pitched roof with a single sloping aspect, resembling half of a gabled roof.

4 Lightweight truss design noted by the curve of the top chord.

5 V-shaped roof style resembling two opposing shed roofs joined along their lower edges.

7 Roof style with characteristics similar to both gambrel and hip roofs.

8 Final outside cover that is placed on top of a roof deck assembly.

9 A second roof constructed over an existing roof.

10 Structure on the roof of a building that may be used as a living space.

13 External covering on a roof that protects the roof from mechanical abrasion.

Chapter 12

Special Structures and Design Features

Terms

Write the definition of the terms below on the blanks provided.

1. High-Rise Building (340) _____

    _____

2. Phase I Operation (350) _____

    _____

3. Phase II Operation (351) _____

    _____

4. Air-Supported Structure (356) _____

    _____

5. Defend in Place (360) _____

    _____

6. Atrium (362) _____

    _____

7. Explosion (364) _____

    _____

8. Area of Refuge (367) _____

    _____

12

Write True or False on the blanks provided; if False, write the correct statement on the lines provided.

_____ 1. A high-rise building is any building that is beyond the effective reach of fire equipment located at the street level. (340)

_____

_____

_____ 2. High-rise buildings as they are known today began to be constructed at the end of the eighteenth century. (341)

_____

_____

_____ 3. High-rise buildings were made possible (and practical) by the developments of steel-frame construction and the elevator. (341)

_____

_____

_____ 4. New York's Empire State Building is 102 stories and was constructed in 1930. (342)

_____

_____

_____ 5. Today, high-rise buildings are constructed of a combination of reinforced concrete and a protected steel frame. (343)

_____

_____

_____ 6. The fire-resistive construction used in high-rise buildings provides a low degree of structural integrity. (343)

_____

_____

_____ 7. In buildings up to 15 or 16 stories, it may be possible to advance hoselines manually up stairwells. (344)

_____

_____

_____ 8. Excessive pressure in the lower portion of a standpipe riser is undesirable because it can make hoselines difficult or dangerous to handle. (344)

_____

_____

_____ 9. Model building and fire codes require fire alarm systems in high-rise buildings. (345)

_____

_____

_____ 10. Model building codes require special mechanical smoke removal provisions from the floor of origin. (346)

_____

_____

_____ 11. The model building codes require a room or area in a high-rise building to serve as a fire command center. (347)

_____

_____

_____ 12. Heating, ventilating, and air conditioning (HVAC) systems in high-rise buildings are designed to provide for the management of products of combustion. (348)

_____

_____

_____ 13. Phase II elevator operation automatically stops all the cars that serve the fire floor if they are moving away from their terminal floor. (350)

_____

_____

_____ 14. To activate Phase I elevator operation, a firefighter must insert a key in a three-position switch within a car to place that particular car in "fire service". (351)

_____

_____

_____ 15. The difficulty in venting heat and smoke is the greatest challenge in controlling fires in underground buildings. (352)

_____

_____

_____ 16. Membrane-covered cable and frame structures rely on air pressure to form the shape of the building. (355)

_____

_____

_____ 17. Modern air-supported roofs have computer-controlled air-supply systems that adjust for varying external wind loads. (356)

_____

_____

_____ 18. Malls are usually designed with one or more large, well-known perimeter stores that are known as anchor stores. (359)

_____

_____

_____ 19. Model building code requirements for fire protection and life safety features for detention and correctional facilities vary depending on the location of the facility. (360)

_____

_____

_____ 20. An explosion can be defined as an event that produces a rapid release of energy. (364)

_____

_____

Short Answer

Write the correct answers on the blanks provided.

1. What are the fire protection features for high-rise buildings that are required by model building codes? (343)

    _____

    _____

    _____

    _____

2. List five features of a fire command center. (347-348)

    _____

    _____

    _____

    _____

    _____

3. List the guidelines for emergency responders for elevator use during a fire. (349)

    _____

    _____

    _____

    _____

    _____

    _____

4. What are the specific difficulties that firefighters face with underground facilities? (352)

    _____

    _____

    _____

    _____

5. List the types of membrane structures. (355)

_____

_____

_____

_____

6. What are the two methods that can be employed to reduce structural damage from an explosion? (365)

_____

_____

Multiple Choice

Write the correct answers on the blanks provided.

_____ 1. Model building codes define a high-rise building as a building more than ___ feet (m) in height. (340)
   A. 25 (8)
   B. 50 (15)
   C. 75 (25)
   D. 100 (30)

_____ 2. The earliest high-rise buildings were rarely more than ___ stories. (342)
   A. 4 or 6
   B. 6 or 8
   C. 8 or 10
   D. 10 or 12

_____ 3. Since the mid ___, building codes have routinely required that high-rise buildings be equipped with automatic sprinkler systems as well as standpipe systems. (343)
   A. 1960's
   B. 1970's
   C. 1980's
   D. 1990's

_____ 4. All model building codes require smokeproof exit enclosures in all stairs serving floors ___ feet (m) or higher. (346)

    A. 25 (8)

    B. 50 (15)

    C. 75 (25)

    D. 100 (30)

_____ 5. Which of the following is an automatic recall of elevators to their terminal floor or an alternate floor that can be caused by the activation of smoke detectors or sprinkler's waterflow alarms? (350)

    A. Phase I

    B. Phase II

    C. Phase III

    D. Phase IV

_____ 6. Which of the following elevator operations is designed to permit firefighters to use the elevators by overriding the recall feature? (351)

    A. Phase I

    B. Phase II

    C . Phase III

    D. Phase IV

_____ 7. An underground building is defined by some codes as one in which the lowest level used for human occupancy is ___ feet (m) below the main exit that serves that level. (352)

    A. 10 (3)

    B. 20 (6)

    C. 30 (10)

    D. 40 (12)

_____ 8. Smokeproof enclosures are now required for buildings with levels more than ___ feet (m) below the level of exit discharge. (353)

    A. 10 (3)

    B. 20 (6)

    C. 30 (10)

    D. 40 (12)

_____ 9. Which of the following is a building in which its exterior skin consists of a thin "waterproof" fabric? (355)

A. Atrium structure

B. Membrane structure

C. Covered mall building

D. Underground building

_____ 10. Codes require individual stores within a shopping mall to have ___ -hour fire-resistive separations from each other. (359)

A. 1

B. 2

C. 3

D. 4

_____ 11. The building codes have a basic requirement that an atrium be enclosed with ___ -hour fire-rated construction of a combination of glass and automatic sprinklers. (362)

A. 1

B. 2

C. 3

D. 4

_____ 12. Which of the following statements regarding rack storage is MOST accurate? (368)

A. Storage racks are frequently arranged with wide aisles.

B. Storage racks are usually stored on wheeled platforms.

C. Storage racks consist of unprotected wooden members.

D. The storage rack system can provide parts of the structural support for the building.

Crossword Puzzle

Across

4 A physical or chemical process that results in the rapid release of high pressure gas into the environment.

5 Emergency elevator operating mode that allows emergency use of the elevator with certain safeguards and special functions.

6 Open area in the center of a building, extending through two or more stories.

7 Procedures taken to shelter persons from harm during an emergency without evacuating them from a structure.

8 Emergency operating mode for elevators; recalls the car to a certain floor and opens the doors.

Down

1 Space in the normal means of egress protected from fire by an approved sprinkler system.

2 Membrane structure that is fully or partially held up by interior air pressure.

3 Any building that requires fire fighting on levels above the reach of the department's equipment.

Chapter 13

Buildings Under Construction, Remodeling, Expansion, and Demolition

Terms

Write the definition of the terms below on the blanks provided.

1. BLEVE (380) _____

   _____

2. Fire Watch (380) _____

   _____

True/False

Write True or False on the blanks provided; if False, write the correct statement on the lines provided.

_____ 1. Frequent site visits by fire inspectors are necessary to keep firefighters familiar with a construction project. (376)

   _____

   _____

_____ 2. Fire codes have requirements for providing adequate access roads before construction begins. (376)

   _____

   _____

_____ 3. Fires frequently occur in the lower floors of high-rise construction projects. (377)

   _____

   _____

_____ 4. Material hoists may be used in place of construction elevators to provide firefighters access to upper floors. (378)

_____

_____

_____ 5. Only two propane cylinders may be stored at construction sites at one time. (380)

_____

_____

_____ 6. Fire watches are often omitted as an economy measure. (380)

_____

_____

_____ 7. A fire-resistive building does not have the structural integrity of a fire-resistive building while under construction. (381)

_____

_____

_____ 8. The most efficient method of providing fire protection on a construction project is to make use of the permanent fire protection systems as they are installed. (383)

_____

_____

_____ 9. Standpipes installed in building projects must be maintained wet during freezing weather. (384)

_____

_____

_____ 10. A renovation project should be planned in such a way that the interruption to sprinkler protection is minimized. (385)

_____

_____

_____ 11. Expansion of buildings most often takes place in large downtown areas. (385)

_____

_____

_____ 12. As a building is demolished, its structural integrity is gradually lost. (387)

_____

_____

Short Answer

Write the correct answers on the blanks provided.

1. What portions of a building are automatic sprinklers sometimes placed in service to protect? (383)

_____

_____

2. What are the practical difficulties with maintaining dry standpipes on construction sites? (384)

_____

_____

_____

_____

Multiple Choice

Write the correct answers on the blanks provided.

_____ 1. Which of the following statements regarding construction site access is MOST accurate? (376)
   A. Parking areas are usually the first phase of a project.
   B. Gates are often open at night and may invite intruders.
   C. Watchmen are present 24 hours a day to open locked gates.
   D. Excavations may make access difficult and driving hazardous.

2. Codes allow the fire department to require the installation of necessary mains and hydrants: (377)
    A. before construction begins.
    B. after construction is complete.
    C. at any point during the construction process.
    D. after the first phase of construction is complete.

3. Which of the following statements regarding fires in high-rise construction projects is MOST accurate? (377-378)
    A. Fires typically begin on the ground floor and move upward.
    B. Normal elevators are usually installed before construction begins.
    C. It can be extremely difficult and dangerous to go up into an uncompleted structure.
    D. Construction elevators are usually operated by an operator that is available 24 hours a day.

4. Newer building codes require that a minimum of ___ lighted stairway(s) be provided when building construction reaches a height above four stories. (379)
    A. 1   C. 3
    B. 2   D. 4

5. Why can electrical wiring become a source of ignition at construction sites? (379-380)
    A. It is subject to thermal damage.
    B. It is moved and rearranged daily.
    C. It is often left live when no one is on-site.
    D. It is often used to power more equipment than can be handled.

6. Which of the following is NOT a danger of heaters at constructions sites? (380)
    A. Burns to workers
    B. Ignition of combustible framework
    C. Fires caused by heaters blown over by the wind
    D. Propane tanks susceptible to mechanical damage

7. Which of the following statements regarding a fire watch is MOST accurate? (380)
    A. The responsible party should have no other duties.
    B. A tour of the facility should be done every 15 minutes.
    C. The responsible party should be provided with a standpipe hose.
    D. A fire watch should be provided before and after welding operations.

8. The most common temporary fire protection measure at a construction site is the installation of: (383)
   A. fire hydrants.
   B. automatic sprinklers.
   C. standpipes with outlets.
   D. fire department connections.

9. Building and fire codes typically require that standpipes be extended before the construction reaches ___ feet (m) above the lowest level of fire department access. (383)
   A. 20 (6.6)
   B. 30 (10)
   C. 40 (13.3)
   D. 50 (15.2)

10. Which of the following statements regarding the hazards of remodeling and renovation is MOST accurate? (384-385)
    A. Construction vehicles often impede fire department access.
    B. The entire automatic sprinkler system is usually shut off for the duration of the work.
    C. The remodeling of a building is usually less hazardous than new construction operations.
    D. Remodeling often takes place in one portion of a building while the remainder of the building continues to be occupied.

11. When expansion of a building is taking place, who should become most familiar with the project? (386)
    A. Fire chief
    B. City manager
    C. City building inspector
    D. First-due fire company

12. Which of the following is a very common cause of fires at buildings being demolished? (387)
    A. Temporary wiring
    B. Cutting with torches
    C. Accumulations of trash
    D. Failure of life safety systems

Chapter 14

Non-Fire Building Collapse

Terms

Write the definition of the terms below on the blanks provided.

1. Subsidence (398) _____

_____

2. Sinkhole (398)_____

_____

True/False

Write True or False on the blanks provided; if False, write the correct statement on the lines provided.

_____ 1. Earthquakes occur most frequently on the East Coast. (394)

_____

_____

_____ 2. Aftershocks are always much weaker than the original earthquake. (396)

_____

_____

_____ 3. Land subsidence is similar to a landslide, but is more gradual. (398)

_____

_____

_____ 4. Sinkholes are usually gradual events. (398)

_____

_____

_____ 5. Tornadoes are more likely in the Midwest. (399)

_____

_____

_____ 6. Building collapse due to snow and water often happens without warning and is usually an isolated event. (401)

_____

_____

_____ 7. Despite building codes and reviews, an inadequate structural design may occur. (403)

_____

_____

_____ 8. Controlled collapse will often require temporary bracing or props. (406)

_____

_____

Short Answer

Write the correct answers on the blanks provided.

1. Name five concerns common to nature-caused collapses. (394)

_____

_____

_____

_____

_____

2. Why has the potential for landslides increased in recent years? (396)

_____

_____

3. What are the general concerns facing firefighters after windstorms, tornadoes, or hurricanes? (400-401)

_____

_____

_____

4. In what two ways does damage resulting from floods occur? (402)

_____

_____

_____

_____

5. What are the main causes of structural collapse during the course of construction? (404)

_____

_____

_____

_____

Mutliple Choice

Write the correct answers on the blanks provided.

_____ 1. Which of the following results from the energy released by a sudden shift in the earth's crust that produces seismic waves? (394)
   A. Landslide   C. Subsidence
   B. Earthquake   D. Seismic shift

_____ 2. Which of the following is the MOST critical factor contributing to the extent of building damage and potential collapse during earthquakes? (396)
   A. Age of the building
   B. Soil conditions beneath the building
   C. Damage sustained by other buildings in the area
   D. Location of building relative to the responsible fault and epicenter of the earthquake

_____ 3. Which of the following is the movement of rock, earth, or debris down a slope? (396)
   A. Sinkhole
   B. Landslide
   C. Earthquake
   D. Subsidence

_____ 4. Which of the following is NOT an early warning sign of a landslide? (397)
   A. Heavy rains
   B. Cracking in roads
   C. Minor slides in the area
   D. Damage to underground utilities

_____ 5. What is the primary cause of a land subsidence in the U.S? (398)
   A. Heavy rains or torrential downpours
   B. Removal of large amounts of underground water
   C. Addition of groundwater through landscape watering
   D. Interaction of ground water with rock formations that are water soluble

_____ 6. In which state do sinkholes more often occur? (398)
   A. Florida
   B. New York
   C. California
   D. Washington

_____ 7. Which of the following resources is most helpful in assisting fire departments in monitoring weather conditions? (399)
   A. Local storm chasers
   B. Local meteorologists
   C. Weather Channel website
   D. NOAA National Weather Services website

_____ 8. In areas where hurricanes with basic wind speed of ___ mph (m/s) or greater are likely, window glazing is required to be impact-resistant. (400)
   A. 70 (31)
   B. 90 (40)
   C. 110 (48)
   D. 130 (58)

9. A change in building use could result in ___, eventually resulting in structural failure. (403)
   A. lower live loads
   B. higher live loads
   C. lower occupancy rates
   D. higher occupancy rates

10. Piecemeal demolition is performed by using: (406)
    A. cranes.
    B. hand tools.
    C. explosives.
    D. wire rope pulling.

11. Which of the following is NOT a common source of explosions in buildings? (406)
    A. Boiler furnaces
    B. Gasoline vapors
    C. Natural gas leaks
    D. Failure of HVAC units

12. Which cause of building collapse is almost always followed by a fire? (407)
    A. Aircraft crash
    B. Careless demolition
    C. Motor vehicle collision
    D. Change in building use

Notes

Notes

Notes

Notes

Notes